MARION WOMAD

A BREATH OF FRESH AIR

John Branfield

Truran

Published by Truran, Croft Prince, Mount Hawke, Truro,
Cornwall TR4 8EE
www.truranbooks.co.uk

©John Branfield 2001

ISBN 1 85022 161 8

Printed and bound in Cornwall by R. Booth (Bookbinders) Ltd
& Troutbeck Press, Antron Hill, Mabe, Penryn,
Cornwall TR10 9HH
Text set in Novarese Medium 10pt.

Cover: detail from Laura Knight *Lamorna Cove* c1917
(Courtsey of Sotheby's)

Author's note

This novel was written in the 1980s. It was put aside and it has only recently come to light. Its themes are still important and relevant, the main difference being the prices. In the novel there is excitement over which Newlyn painter would break the £100,000 barrier; today a Stanhope Forbes painting has sold for over a million pounds.

It is a work of fiction but is full of information about the Newlyn painters. Many Newlyn School paintings can be seen at:

Falmouth Art Gallery
Penlee House Gallery and Museum, Penzance
Plymouth City Art Gallery
Royal Cornwall Museum, Truro

A BREATH OF FRESH AIR

1

SNOWSCAPES

Samuel John Lamorna Birch RA
Tranquility
Oil on canvas, 42$^1/_2$ x 60 in
Signed
Exhibited: Royal Academy, 1926

A cold green river, its banks thickly encrusted with snow, flows around the bottom of a bowl-shaped landscape. A few bare trees stand tall, the base of their trunks in shadow, the tops catching a wintry sunlight.

Molly pops in for a moment, shattering the calm of the morning. "It's only me," she calls. "I've just popped in for a moment."

When she comes down the stairs she is pulling on her coat. I have come out of the study.

"You shouldn't have left your desk," she says. "I didn't want to disturb you."

"I wondered what was happening."

"I only wanted an extra jumper, there's a bitterly cold east wind. It's drifting the snow."

"Would you like a cup of coffee?"

"No, I've had several already. Everyone wants to offer me tea or coffee because of the weather."

"What's it like out?"

"I'll tell you at lunch time, I must get on."

"Are the roads passable?"

"They're not too bad. I've got to go, you're trying to keep me."

"Have you spoken to the Hoopers yet?"

"You're making excuses, Roger. You should be at your desk."

"Are you going there now?"

"I'll see you at one," she calls. The door slams, and she is gone.

I return to my study, and a deep quiet settles down over the house. I look out of the window. The lawn is covered with the snow that has fallen during the night, the first of the year. It lies thick on the branches of the trees and the wind scatters it in fresh falls. Its weight bows down the gorse bushes on the stone hedge.

I can't work this morning, I can't get on at all. There's a story I should be writing; I have it clear in my mind. But the thought of putting pen to paper is hateful. The sheet in front of me remains as untouched as the lawn beyond the window. I want to be outside, walking to the gate and leaving my footprints in the snow.

They would have been outside, the plein-air painters of around the turn of the century. They would have relished the snow, making the most of it while it lasted. In their thick tweeds and long greatcoats, in boots and deerstalker hats, they would have painted and sketched as the snow flurried around them. They would have delighted in the restricted palette, the changed light cast over the landscape, the touches of colour in the yellow flowers of the gorse or the red berries of the firethorn.

And yet when you think about it, not many of them painted snowscapes. The scenes that you associate with the Newlyn school are scenes of high summer. Horses drink from leafy watering places. Cattle stand in long grass. People sit out of doors in the dappled sunlight under the trees, reading books or painting at easels. The gardens are full of flowers, hollyhocks or anemones. Inside the houses the sun shines through the windows and the women wear summer frocks. On the beach girls in sunbonnets paddle at the water's edge. Boys bathe from rowing boats or dive from the rocks. It seems that it was one long summer, that morning always filled the bowl of Lamorna Cove.

Some of the painters were holiday visitors. But those who lived in West Cornwall throughout the year did not record many snowfalls. There are no Stanhope Forbes paintings of snow scenes, as far as I know. Nor are there any Gotches or Garstins or Harold Harveys. I could imagine an Elizabeth Forbes, a girl in a red fur-lined hood and cape against a background of snow, but I don't think she ever painted it. A Tuke snow scene is inconceivable; his subjects were ships and the sea and naked youths. A painter like Charles Simpson, with his interest in wildlife, would surely have gone out to see the flocks of birds that arrive with the snow, the redwings and fieldfares, the snipe and woodcock and plovers. But in all his sketches and book illustrations, I can't think of any with snow in them. Where are the dunlin frozen to death, the foxes hunting for food in the snow, the stackyards in winter?

There was a snow scene by Laura Knight in the second Newlyn exhibition: it showed Cheyne Walk in London. I look it up in the catalogue, which quotes her description of how she painted it. 'I set up my easel on the Embankment.... And stayed there all day despite the cold and having to hold my easel with one hand and paint with the other, but I finished my large watercolour in which a scarlet pillar-box was a prominent feature.' It was shown at the Royal Academy in 1909.

Alfred Munnings did a painting of foxhounds being fed in the snow, and a view of his garden under snow at Dedham in Suffolk. Apart from these, painted away from Cornwall, it seems that the Newlyn artists – with one exception – did not paint snowscapes.

The exception is Lamorna Birch. He alone delighted in the snow and *Lingering Snows*, 1906 is the only other snow scene in the two Newlyn exhibitions. It is a large oil on canvas of cold-blue pine trees beneath a copper-coloured sky, a snow-filled lane disappearing into the distance.

I start looking through my catalogues. Another canvas of the same year is *Driving Sheep in the Snow*. What really interests Birch is the snow, and the shepherd driving his sheep is included because he feels that he ought, like Stanhope Forbes, to be depicting the activities of rural life; the sheep are diminished in scale and look more like a flock of woolly mice. You can feel how crunchy the snow is. If English had eleven words for snow, as the Inuit language is supposed to have, you would know which one to use to describe the snow in a Lamorna Birch painting.

He often spent so long painting in the cold that his family feared for his health. His daughter Mornie remembers one particularly cold day when he was painting outside his studio, dressed in plus-fours with thick woollen stockings and mittens. When she expressed concern, he asked her to fetch him 'a bun and a mug of cocoa'.

I look up and read Laura Knight's description of him as he was when she first met him in Cornwall in 1907. 'I remember the brownish tweeds he wore – and a rather battered hat, a tweed homburg with a host of artificial fishing flies stuck in it. He was slender of build and tallish of height; his beard and hair were dark brown; his face was tanned; his cheeks were rosy; his skin was smooth and fine; and a full generous mouth showed beneath his moustache. His knickerbockers, strapped and buckled just below the knee, allowed the display, as he came down the hill, of his splendidly developed legs, the calves of which could have been the envy of any man... But the nicest feature about the whole of John, as we used to call him, was his radiant friendly look and smile.'

I imagine this robust, extrovert character setting out on his thickly-stockinged, well-developed legs into the snow, eager to get on with the work of recording the changes made by the light to the landscape. He was a most prolific artist. Even on holiday he would continue to paint. During his final illness he would be helped from his bed to the window, where a watercolour box and paper awaited him, and he would record once more the valley and the cove below the house.

But I can't get on at all, I don't feel at all prolific, not at all like Lamorna Birch. I leave the study to go and look at one of his paintings. There are pictures in every room, several Simpsons of birds and animals and children, a few oil sketches by Stanhope Forbes, two Procters and a Gotch, watercolours by Fred Evans and Henry Scott Tuke. The light reflected from the snow outside fills the house and the paintings are changed, bright and magical.

The Birch is in one of the bedrooms. It came from his studio at Flagstaff Cottage, the house overlooking Lamorna Cove that he bought when he married and where he lived until his death. He took the name 'Lamorna' because he loved the valley and the cove, and to distinguish himself from the older Newlyn painter, Lionel Birch. He also called his daughter Lamorna, or 'Mornie', and it was from her that I bought the painting. It was the only one that she had of the cove, though it was covered with dust and cobwebs. I took it home and washed it in warm water. The grime disappeared and the granite quarry in the background of the picture showed pink and blue.

I stand and look at it now, in the albescent light. It has the bowl-shaped structure that Birch was fond of; from the cliff-path it looks back across the water to the quarry above the cove. Unusually for Birch, it contains figures; a young woman, with her fair hair coiled in 'earphones' in the style of the twenties, sits on a bank of grass before an easel, her legs stretched out in front of her. In her white artist's smock she looks as sculptured and solid as the rocks; even her canvas looks as though it is made of stone. The model she is painting is a young girl with bobbed hair sitting on a rock in the lower centre of the picture with the cove behind her; her separateness from the landscape is emphasised by the viridian green of her dress. The rocks gleam white, the areas of pure colour, the blue of the sea and the green of shallow water, glow in the sunlight.

The young woman with her hair in coils is Midge Bruford, a student of Birch's and a school friend of Mornie's. While staying at Flagstaff Cottage she meets the artist Richard Weatherby, who has returned from service with the Essex Yeomanry during the war. According to the catalogue, they go and live together at Bochym Manor, an old stone house on the Lizard peninsula. Weatherby is master of the Cury Harriers and the stables are filled with horses and hounds. In their studios Midge paints goats and gipsy caravans, Richard paints hunting scenes in the style of his friend Munnings. But the liaison does not last. Richard marries Karenza Boscawen, cousin of Lord Falmouth, and Midge moves with her animals to a cottage near Mousehole.

It's not quite true, of course. The cataloguers gleaned their information from Weatherby's nephew, who was a boy at the time. Her surviving sister is most indignant; Midge never lived with Weatherby, though she was engaged to him for a while. Harold Harvey, who was in love with her, did a painting entitled – oddly – *Midge Bruford and Fiancé*. He placed a gate between them.

But it would make a good story. It's a period romance, a novel that Daphne du Maurier might have written. Scenes from it begin to unfold in my head. My mind seems full of other people's lives, other people's creativity...

"Where are you?" Molly's voice rings cheerfully through the cold house. The morning has gone before I know it; nothing passes the time more quickly than looking at catalogues and pictures. I come down the stairs.

"What were you doing?" she asks, taking pens and thermometers out of the breast pocket of her dress.

"I was looking at the Lamorna Birch."

"I thought you might have set the table," she says. "What have you been doing all morning?"

"I looked at some catalogues."

"You're too easily distracted."

"I became interested in Birch and looked up a few facts."

"Have you done any writing?"

"I've thought about a novel." It doesn't sound very convincing. "A country house in the twenties, a woman artist and her two lovers..."

"And you call that a morning's work?"

"It doesn't sound much."

We set the table, put out the bread and soup, and sit down to eat. "How have you got on?" I ask.

"I've had a terrible morning," she says.

"What happened?"

"I couldn't get down to Mrs Hicks. There was a snowdrift at the top of the lane, it had blown through an open gateway and piled up. I drove straight into it and came to a stop. I had to get out and walk the rest of the way. Then I made her some porridge for breakfast, she was only having cornflakes and it was so cold. That delayed me and I've been rushing to catch up ever since."

"What are the roads like?"

"A bit slippery, but not too bad. I avoided the hill as I knew I wouldn't get up it again, but that took ages, going all the other way round. And then when I got to the Tiddys' I thought at least the geese would be shut inside in this weather. But as soon as I opened the gate they came for me, three great white birds with their necks out, hissing like mad."

I picture the geese, their wings flapping against the snow, goose feathers and snowflakes flying in the air; it would have been a subject for Charles Simpson. "What did you do?"

"I waited for Edward to come out. I told him, if he doesn't keep those geese in – they're ganders really – I'll refuse to visit his mother and he'll have to take her to the surgery every day for her injection. I felt a bit mean, but they're worse than dogs, I can cope with *them*. But geese ..." She shudders. "At least the yard was frozen, so I didn't have to wade through all the mud as usual."

She holds her bowl of soup with both hands, to warm them.

"Have you been to see the Hoopers yet?" I ask.

"No, I haven't," says Molly.

"Are you going to?"

"I'm far too busy."

The Hoopers have been on my mind for a while. They live in a large Victorian house behind stone walls at the end of the village street. I have heard of a Denzil Hooper, a father or uncle, who once lived there. In the registers that Henry Scott Tuke kept throughout his life of all his paintings, there is an entry in 1927 for a *Beach Study*, exhibited at the Royal Academy and sold for twenty-five guineas to Denzil Hooper.

It seems unlikely that there were two Denzil Hoopers. Whenever I walk past the house and glimpse through the iron gates its curtained windows, I wonder if the beach study is still there. At twenty-five guineas, it would be an oil painting, but not a large one, a full-figure study of a young man with the sea in the background. I wonder how he is posed. Is he standing with an oar over his shoulder? Is he sitting on the rocks, reading a book or looking out to sea? Is he drying himself with a towel after a swim?

I wonder what condition it is in and whether it has its original frame. It is tantalising to know that the picture is probably there, so near and yet so far. Ever since discovering the reference, I have wanted Molly to find an excuse for calling on them. I only want to know what it looks like.

"Don't you think they need a visit, this cold weather?" I suggest.

"The doctors haven't asked me."

"But you can visit on your own initiative."

"I've enough work on my hands, without looking for extra," she says. "And anyway, you're only interested in their Tuke."

"I'd like to know if it's still there."

"I've got other things to do than go around looking at pictures."

It is surprising how many valuable paintings there are within the area of the two surgeries that the community nurses cover. I know – through Molly – where there are several Stanhope Forbes, an Elizabeth Forbes, a Frank Bramley, a Walter Langley, several Gotches, a superb Lamorna Birch. If I ever thought of becoming a dealer – which I am not, of course – we would make an ideal team.

"Are you going back to work this afternoon?" asks Molly.

"No, it's too late now."

"What will you do?"

"I'll have a walk."

"It's all right for some," says Molly. "You give in too easily."

She finishes her meal quickly; she has only stayed

ten minutes. "I'm off then," she says. "I want to get back before it starts freezing again."

"Where are you going now?"

She is struggling into her coat. "I'm going to see Mrs Baragwaneth."

She is the lady who owns the Lamorna Birch.

"Offer her five hundred pounds for her painting," I call after her.

"I'll do no such thing," she says, and slams the door.

At Flagstone Cottage, Lamorna Birch had a beautiful Tuke, the gift of the artist; it showed a white ship with three masts, a clipper on a hazy sea.

I fetch my cap, coat and walking stick. The dog jumps up from beside the kitchen stove and hurtles herself at the door. She runs out into the snow, her legs skidding beneath her.

I breathe in the cold, fresh air. My boots crunch through the snow on the footpath in the valley. I am the first person to pass this way today and the snow lies smooth between the hedges, broken only by the fresh footprints of the dog and a few animal and bird tracks. The birds' feet mark arrows in the snow and there are the prints of a fox running up and down close to the bank.

The bushes overhanging the path, hawthorn, blackthorn and wild plum, are filled with snow and each branch and twig stands out clearly. Everything is black and white, as in a woodcut. It is bright in the normally dark tunnel between the trees. Where the path comes out on to the hillside, the snow has drifted, building up into knee-deep drifts every twenty yards. The dog sinks into them, leaping like a dolphin to pass through. The gorse bushes bend beneath impossible loads.

At this time of year I don't expect the countryside to

be colourful, but when I see it now totally drained of any hue, I realise how much colour there generally is, even in winter: the rich purple of dead bracken soaked by the rain, the orange tips to the willows, the pink spill of mine waste from a burrow. Now everything is in monochrome.

The lake is frozen; it reflects the metallic grey of the sky. A flock of lapwings passes slowly up the valley, as I walk on down towards the cove. There are ice-shapes along the sides of the stream, where the spray from an impeding stone or a small fall of rock has frozen on the overhanging vegetation, clustering in thick fingers.

The tide is out. I walk through snow to the high-water mark; there is ice amongst the rocks and pebbles. Large flocks of gulls stand motionless on the shore. The stream falling into the cave has turned into a frozen waterfall; long spears of ice hang from the ledges. I won't stand underneath, fearful of being impaled by an icy shaft.

As the dog runs down to the water's edge, the gulls lift into the air. They rise in one regular unfurling movement and their wings flap in a pattern of brown and white, black and white. They settle further away on the sand, below the headland covered with snow.

2
ARTISTS OF THE NEWLYN SCHOOL
1880-1950
a chronology

Stanhope Alexander Forbes RA
The Drinking Place
Oil on canvas, 69¹/₂ x 60¹/₂ *in*
Signed and dated, Stanhope A Forbes 1900
Exhibited: *Royal Academy* 1900
OLDHAM ART GALLERY

A farm worker brings two horses to the pool to drink, perhaps at the end of a morning's work. The light shines through the trees and is reflected from the water on to horse and man.

1882   Walter Langley settles in Newlyn, soon followed by Edwin Harris; both artists are from Birmingham.

1884   In January Stanhope Forbes takes the train from Paddington to Falmouth. 'I had just returned from Brittany, and was looking for a fresh sketching ground. A friend suggested the Cornish coast. We settled at Manaccan, on the other side of Mount's Bay, but finding the place lacked interest for a figure painter I took my knapsack, went exploring on my own account, and ultimately found myself in Newlyn.' He writes home that 'Newlyn is a sort of English Concarneau and is the haunt of a great many painters.' Thomas Cooper Gotch and Leghe Suthers have temporarily left; others in Newlyn are Ralph Todd, Fred Hall, Frank Bramley and Percy Craft. Later in the year they are joined by

Fred Millard, WJ Wainwright, Henry Scott Tuke, Chevallier Tayler, Blandford Fletcher and Frank Bodilly. By 4th September *The Cornishman* notes that there are no less than twenty-seven artists residing in Newlyn. Some settle, some come and go, as they did in the Breton village of Pont Aven.

1885 Henry Detmold, William Fortescue and the Canadian artist Elizabeth Adela Armstrong, accompanied by her mother, stay in Newlyn.

Stanhope Forbes: A *Fish Sale on a Cornish Beach* is a triumph at the Royal Academy.

1886 Tuke buys *Julie of Nantes*, a French brigantine which he uses as a floating studio.

Norman Garstin settles in Newlyn.

The New English Art Club, in which Forbes, Gotch and Tuke are involved, is formed as an alternative to the Royal Academy.

1887 Thomas Cooper Gotch and his wife Caroline Yates settle in Newlyn at the Malt House, later moving to Trewarveneth Farm and then to Wheal Betsy.

1888 Frank Bramley: A *Hopeless Dawn* is exhibited at the Royal Academy and bought for the nation by the Chantrey Bequest. It becomes one of the best-known British paintings. Stanhope Forbes: *The Village Philharmonic.*

'The Newlyners are the most significant body of painters now in England.' Alice Meynell, in a review of the RA exhibition, makes the earliest reference to 'the Newlyn School'.

Arthur Bateman buys a field in Newlyn and builds the first of the 'glass houses' or studios. The practice is begun of having a studio 'open day' once a year in March.

1889 Stanhope Forbes: *The Health of the Bride* is bought by Henry Tate. Stanhope Forbes marries Elizabeth Armstrong in August, against the advice of his mother.

Henry Scott Tuke: "All Hands to the Pumps!" is 'crowded out' at the Royal Academy.

The first record of the annual cricket match between the painters of Newlyn and those of St. Ives: FW Bourdillon describes it as 'a very jolly day and a most exciting finish'.

Samuel John Birch, twenty years old, a clerk, linoleum designer and self-taught painter, arrives in Cornwall from Lancashire with £25 and his belongings in a tin trunk. He lodges at Boleigh Farm, at the head of the Lamorna valley.

1890   Stanhope Forbes: By Order of the Court.

The Newlyn Industrial Class is started by JD Mackenzie to retrain young fishermen in new skills, mainly copperwork, during a recession in the fishing industry.

1892   Stanhope Forbes: Forging the Anchor.

1893   Henry Scott Tuke: August Blue is exhibited at the Royal Academy and bought by the Chantrey Bequest.

1894   The opening of the North Pier at Newlyn.

1895   The Passmore Edwards Gallery is opened.

Frank Bramley leaves Newlyn.

1898   Harold Harvey, who has grown up in Penzance and been a student of Norman Garstin, first exhibits at the Royal Academy.

1899   Henry Scott Tuke: The Diver is exhibited at the Royal Academy.

Stanhope Forbes founds his school for the teaching of painting.

Alfred Munnings first exhibits at the Royal Academy, Pike Fishing in January and Stranded. He sees his first horse race, and loses the sight of one eye in an accident.

1900   Stanhope Forbes: The Drinking Place is exhibited at the Royal Academy and bought by Oldham Art Gallery. In a lecture to the Royal Cornwall Polytechnic Society, he speaks of the plein-air movement as 'a breath of fresh air in the tired atmosphere of the studio'.

Henry Scott Tuke: Ruby, Gold and Malachite is exhibited at the Royal Academy and bought by the London Corporation.

1902 Lamorna Birch marries his pupil, Emily Houghton Vivian, nicknamed 'Mouse', and moves into Flagstaff Cottage, Lamorna.

1904 Stanhope Forbes builds and moves into Higher Faugan.

1905 Charles Simpson first exhibits at the Royal Academy: *Autumn Ploughing*.

1907 Harold and Laura Knight arrive, attracted by the reputation of the Newlyn School.

1908 Alfred Munnings pays the first of many visits to Cornwall. Laura Knight writes: 'never had I come across such an overwhelming vitality... I could not take my eyes off him, he was the stable, the artist, the poet, the very land itself... I adored everything about him.' He immediately organises parties, picnics and outings.

Harold Knight's first Newlyn paintings: A *Village Wedding* and *In the Spring*, which shows a couple taking tea in dappled sunlight beneath apple trees in blossom.

1909 Laura Knight: *The Beach*, her first large work painted in Newlyn, is exhibited at the Royal Academy. 'Who is this Laura Knight?' asks Mrs Asquith.

1910 Stanhope Forbes and Chevallier Tayler are elected Royal Academicians.

1912 Elizabeth Forbes dies.

Ernest Procter marries Dod Shaw at Newlyn; both have been students at the Forbes School of Painting.

Laura and Harold Knight move from Newlyn to Trewarveneth Farm, following the Forbeses and the Gotches. Later they move to 'Oakhill' at Lamorna. 'For the first time in our lives we possessed a house of our own, a cook, a parlour-maid, and a gardener; we were equipped even to a lawn mower.'

Alfred Munnings marries Florence Carter-Wood, also an artist, and they settle at Cliff house, Lamorna. He buys a cow to use as a model.

Impressed by Roger Fry's second Post-Impressionist exhibition, Frank Dobson, a student of Forbes, finds his methods old-fashioned. Forbes is shocked by his 'modernism'.

1913 Charles Simpson marries Ruth Alison, a student at Forbes's school. They live first at Newlyn before moving to Lamorna and then to St Ives, where they run a painting school.

Laura Knight begins *Lamorna Birch and His Daughters*, a 7'6" x 9' canvas completed in 1934.

Alfred Munnings does a series of paintings at Zennor, staying at a farm with his groom and model, Ned Osborne, and two mares, Grey Tick and The Duchess.

1914 Florence Munnings dies after taking cyanide.

During the war Alfred Munnings trains army horses at Reading, and then goes to France as an official war artist attached to the Canadian Cavalry Brigade. He paints a mounted portrait of General Seely (1918).

Cedric Morris, unfit for military service, helps Munnings train horses.

Stanhope Forbes marries Maudie Palmer, a former pupil (1915).

His son Alex is killed in action.

Charles Simpson is kept from military service by the riding accident which has earlier prevented him from following a military career.

Charles Naper serves in France.

Ernest Procter joins the Friends' Ambulance unit and serves in France.

Harold Knight is a conscientious objector and works on the land.

1918 Laura and Harold Knight move to London, but keep studios at Lamorna for summer holidays.

1919 Alfred Munnings: *Epsom Downs – City and Suburban Day*.

He buys Castle House, Dedham, and meets his second wife, Violet McBridge. His portrait of General Seely leads to many commissions.

1920 Ernest and Dod Procter are commissioned to decorate the Kokine Palace in Rangoon, Burma, belonging to the Chinese millionaire, Ching Tsong.

1922 Harold Harvey: *The Critics* is exhibited at the Royal Academy.

Alfred Munnings: *The Grey Horse*, one of the Zennor paintings, is exhibited at the Royal Academy and sells for nine hundred guineas.

Charles Simpson: *The Flight of the Wild Duck* is awarded a silver medal at the Paris Salon.

1924 Charles Simpson: *The Herring Season*.

1925 Dod Procter: *The Model* is exhibited at the Royal Academy. 'The Model gave the London public an idea of what the painting of the future is going to be like.' (The Observer)

1926 Lamorna Birch: *Morning Fills the Bowl* is exhibited at the Royal Academy.

Alfred Munnings becomes a Royal Academician.

1927 Dod Procter: *Morning* is exhibited at the Royal Academy and named 'Painting of the Year'. It is bought by the Daily Mail for the Tate Gallery. On Dod's return to Newlyn, flags are hung in celebration of her success and she is led from the station by a silver band.

1928 In the month of February, *Morning* is seen in Birmingham by over sixty thousand visitors.

1929 Laura Knight is made a Dame of the British Empire. Henry Scott Tuke dies.

1934 Lamorna Birch is elected Royal Academician.

Ernest Procter is appointed director of studies in Design and Craft at the Glasgow School of Art.

1935 Ernest Procter dies.

1936 Laura Knight becomes a Royal Academician. She

publishes her autobiography, *Oil Paint and Grease Paint.*

1937 Harold Knight becomes a Royal Academician.

1944 Alfred Munnings is elected President of the Royal Academy and is knighted.

1947 Stanhope Forbes dies in Penzance at the age of ninety.

3

MAKING A LIVING

the artist as businessman

Samuel John Lamorna Birch RA
The Thaw
Watercolour, 7¼ x 10½ in
Signed
Exhibited: Fine Art Society, London, 1908

A few patches of snow remain on the slopes of the Lamorna valley, away from the sea, though the distant hills are white.

The snow has almost disappeared; only a little is left along the bottom of north-facing hedges. It is no longer freezing by mid-afternoon and Molly is in no hurry to dash off after lunch.

"I've finished the story," I say.

"That surprises me," she says. "Whenever I've seen you at work recently you seem to be making lists."

"I made a chronology of the Newlyn School."

"What use is that?"

"Nobody's done it before, it shows up all sorts of interest."

"Such as?"

"The way there's a cycle to all things, whether an artist or a movement. They grow, flourish and then die away."

"You're so pessimistic!"

"No, it's just organic."

"There's no need for *you* to give up yet."

"I'm not." I try to be more positive. "It also shows the affect of the first world war. It would make a good novel: a girl comes to Newlyn as a student of Forbes, enjoys the social life of the artists, falls in love with a fellow painter – and then the idyll is brought to an end by the outbreak of war."

"You can't use a chronology," says Molly. She starts to read the manuscript of the short story.

Twenty-three books I've written all together, though not one of them is a novel. First came the three collections of short stories on which my reputation is based, and then I wrote the thirteen books of MORNING FILLS THE BOWL: *the Travail family saga*. It was a series about how we escaped from the London rat-race and returned to the peace of the Cornish countryside, about the children growing up with their pet animals, our holidays at sea in an old gaff-rigged yawl. I brought out six or seven books on local subjects; I even wrote a book – it was not much more than a list really – about the painters of the Newlyn school, *An Artist on Every Corner*, in the days when their reputation was at its lowest. It has since become a collectors' item, probably because of the illustrations. I tried to buy a copy recently in a secondhand bookshop, as I had given away or lost all mine. They wanted forty pounds for it, for my own book! I didn't buy it.

I edited *Cornubia*, the south-west literary magazine, for twenty years and I've written reviews and articles. Like the Newlyn painters, I've plugged away at it, writing every day. But now the fifth and last child has left home and the boat is sold. I don't feel that I have much left to write about.

Molly turns the last page. "Is that all?" she asks in surprise.

"That's it."

"I thought it would be longer, I thought you said something about a novel, something like Daphne du Maurier."

"It didn't work out."

"That's a shame."

"Well," I ask, "what do you think of it?"

"I like it very much," says Molly loyally. "One thing I'm glad about, for once you haven't put me into it. I'm fed up with reading about myself."

"It's never you anyway."

"No, but everyone thinks it is. And I'm not sure some of the time, whether it's really me or not... Who is the woman meant to be?"

"No one in particular."

"I suppose the painter is Lamorna Birch."

"No, of course not, you can't say things like that."

"Because you can't use real people, can you?" says Molly. "Though that's never stopped you using me."

"That's different."

"You mean they could sue and I couldn't."

I try to explain. "It's a story, it's made up. It's about having a collection, the responsibility that brings and also the sense of identity that it gives."

"So what will you do with it?"

"I don't know. I'll put it aside, I suppose, and start something else."

They worked hard, the professional painters in Cornwall around the turn of the century. They kept at it every day, out in all weathers or working at pictures in their studios. Henry Scott Tuke and Charles Napier Hemy both converted ships into floating studios, so that they could work at sea. Elizabeth Forbes had a portable glass studio which could be moved from place to place. Charles Simpson rode a motorcycle combination, in the sidecar of which he carried his easel and canvases to wherever he was painting. Besides producing pictures, they gave lessons and illustrated books; they even wrote them.

What am I going to write now? I wonder, when Molly has gone back to work. That isn't a bad idea, a novel about student painters in Newlyn. It's all right for the artist, he can go on painting the same subject, his wife or his friends or his favourite landscape, for year after year. But the writer always has to find something new.

How I envy the painters, men like Forbes or Birch or Tuke. They were able to do what they enjoyed and yet make a reasonable living. Henry Scott Tuke got it just right. He would spend the winter in London, fulfilling portrait commissions and preparing work for the Royal Academy. He liked to travel abroad in the spring, usually to the south of France and to Italy. He was always in Falmouth for the summer, staying at his cottage on Pennance Point. He painted on the secluded beach below the house or on board the *Julie of Nantes*.

Stanhope Forbes visited his floating studio in 1887; I look up the letter he wrote immediately afterwards to his mother. 'Tuke showed us his pictures which are simply beautiful. Gave us a wonderful tea under stranger conditions than ever I took that meal before. It is a strange life to lead and only a man like Tuke could do it, but it suits him exactly, and he has subjects all round him such as he likes to paint best of all. We left him at last delighted with his ship and his work.'

Tuke loved the open-air life. He enjoyed all sports, especially cricket and bicycling; he loved sailing almost as much as painting. At first he brought professional models from London; later many of the local youths sat for him, fisherlads and dockyard apprentices. One of his favourite models, Johnny Jackett, played rugby for Cornwall and England.

He managed to express his interest in young men in an age when it was impossible to be open about homosexuality. Oscar Wilde – whom Tuke had met when studying in Paris – was tried and found guilty of offences against morality in 1895, the year after *August Blue* was bought for the nation. It did not discourage Tuke from painting naked boys. When *The Diver* was exhibited at the Royal Academy in 1899, the reviewer of the *Cornish Echo*, responding to the mood of the time, wrote: 'Mr Tuke seems to find nothing so congenial to his mind as to tackle a subject everybody else would shrink from... Masterly as is Mr Tuke's work, one cannot help feeling regret that he does not give his attention to a more acceptable subject.' In 1902 he exhibited *Ruby, Gold and Malachite*, in which the sun shines on the golden limbs of five naked bathers, whilst a sixth boy in a ruby-red shirt sits at the oars of a rowing boat on a malachite sea.

He produced, according to the registers, one thousand two hundred and sixty-nine paintings. He could sell them all, from one pound for an early portrait – 'a quid' he entered in the register – to £525 for *August Blue*. 'Swelled head' he noted in his diary; it was the second of his paintings to be bought by the Chantrey bequest, an almost unprecedented compliment. His small watercolours sold for three to five guineas, a small oil from twenty pounds upwards.

I have just one Tuke painting, a watercolour of boats moored in Falmouth harbour and dated 1907. It is not entered in the registers, as far as I can tell; it might be one of the 'FOUR WATERCOLOUR SKETCHES to Helman, and Falmouth Gallery, £8-10'. I bought it for a few pounds, though if I were a dealer I would ask four hundred.

But I'm not selling it, of course. I enjoy having this small link with Tuke's life. I would like to have one of his oils. I wonder what the Hoopers' picture is like, if it's still in their house. I'd give almost anything for a good example of his work, like the white ship that once belonged to Lamorna Birch. But it would be far more than I could ever afford.

In the post is an envelope with the logo of a famous publishing house, not one that I have ever had any dealings with. I turn it over a few times, but do not let my hopes rise. After all, I have never submitted anything to them. They probably want to sell me something, a subscription to a magazine or an entry in a biographical dictionary with an order form for a copy at a special pre-publication price of $300. But this firm does not publish magazines nor works of reference.

I slit it open. It is a request for permission to include a short story I wrote many years ago in a collection that they are publishing. I feel pleased that the story has not been forgotten.

I read on: 'We hope that you will consider a fee of £40 satisfactory. It would be paid on publication, together with a complimentary copy of the book.'

It is extra income without extra work, but forty pounds is not very much. I try to live by what I produce; I've never accepted any grants or subsidies, or collected a regular salary. It's been a struggle. I could never have managed if there hadn't been one or two windfalls, if Molly hadn't always worked. Sometimes in a year I have made more than she has, but her salary is consistent; generally I have made less, especially in recent years.

I shall not get a pension. Now, as I approach retirement age, I begin to think about this, like the man in the advertisement. Will I still be able to produce in my old age?

Stanhope Forbes went on painting and exhibiting until he was ninety, Lamorna Birch well into his eighties. Their work declined, but it still sold. I suspect that it is easier to go on painting, just out of habit, than it is to write.

I pick up the phone and ring the publishers. I express my disappointment at their offer. They say that it is in line with others in the same book, but that they are willing to increase it to sixty pounds. I am pleased to accept.

Encouraged by this success, I look out my folder of unpublished stories. I have eight to which I can add the one I have just finished. I wanted to make them up to twelve, the number in each of the collections, but nine will have to do. I decide to send them to my publisher straight away.

4

DADDY'S PAINTING
a short story by Roger Trevail

Daniel Brent RA
Girl on a Swing
Oil on canvas, 36 x 24 in
Exhibited: Royal Academy, 1927
THE ARTIST'S DAUGHTER

The invitation came in the post. As Dorothy Brent drew the card out of the envelope, she saw reproduced on it the painting that had hung for years on her bedroom wall. How different it seemed! She had never really looked at it before.

It showed herself as a child, sixty years ago, sitting on a swing in dappled sunlight. It was odd, she thought, that no one had seen it for all that time, and now it would be on public display.

She turned the card over. She was invited to the private viewing in London of the exhibition which included her father's portrait of her. She wouldn't be able to go, of course. She rarely left the house. There was so much to do, trying to maintain it as it had been when her father was alive. It was far too large for one person living alone, a stone and slate house in a valley by the sea, with Daddy's studio at the bottom of the orchard. Her parents had always employed a housekeeper and a gardener. Now she did it all herself, with no help indoors and just a man who came two afternoons a week in summer to mow the grass and cut the hedges.

Daddy had been very attached to the place and she felt that she had to keep it up. It had been the subject of so many of his paintings, the house above the mass of apple blossom in the valley, the stream which flowed through the woods to the beach, the cliffs and the sea. Many of them showed her as a child, perching in the bough of a tree, paddling on the beach or sitting on top of a sandcastle. They had become quite fashionable again.

She would have liked to accept, she saw so few people. She liked company, but when her mother had died, over thirty years ago, she had given up her job in London and come home to look after her father. For many years she had missed her own little flat and the comradeship of the office. At home there were few opportunities to make friends. When her mother had been alive, the house had been full of people, artists and writers. But Daddy had grieved for her and given up exhibiting. He had been very demanding, particularly during his long illness at the end. She had never married.

But she had made the best of it. She drove a car, thank goodness. She had had to learn, to take Daddy around with his easel and canvases, for he had always painted out of doors and he had never learned to drive. It meant that she could pick up her few friends, play golf occasionally. If she wanted a holiday she stayed with cousins in Northamptonshire, and in summer they would visit her in Cornwall.

The renewed interest in the artists of the twenties had brought more visitors. The first was a young man called Jeremy who spent a few afternoons at the house, looking at the paintings and selecting half a dozen for the exhibition. He introduced her to Marilyn who was researching a book on the art of the period. She had returned several times to study Daddy's scrapbooks and diaries, and talk about him. Dorothy felt that she had made two good friends.

She placed the invitation on the mantelpiece, as her mother used to do – how full of cards it had once been! – and went upstairs to the indoors studio, the room where Daddy had worked towards the end of his life when he could no longer walk to the studio in the orchard. As a young man he had painted a lot of the furniture in the house, decorating it with designs of shells and flowers, and now after more than half a century it had faded. She was trying to restore a small chest of drawers, mixing colours to get something like the original shade.

The telephone rang. She balanced the brush on the paint-pot and went down to the hall to answer.

"Dorothy Brent?" enquired a cultured, male voice.

"Yes."

"Have you received your invitation?"

"It came this morning."

"I'm so glad," said the man. He went on to talk about the exhibition, how he thought Daniel Brent's paintings were the most exciting of the whole group.

Dorothy wondered who he was. From the way he talked, he seemed to have something to do with organizing the exhibition. "Who are you?" she asked.

"My name's Helman," he said. "I'm a great friend of Jeremy's, he's been talking to me about your collection of pictures. Do you think I could possibly see them?"

"The best ones have gone to the exhibition."

"I'd love to see the others. I'm in the area, would this afternoon be convenient?"

"Yes, if you like," said Dorothy. After all, he was a friend of Jeremy's.

It was snowing when the large grey car came up the drive soon after lunch. Two men got out and hurried to the door. They looked very smart in their city clothes, she thought. Helman had silver hair and a florid complexion; he wore a black overcoat with an astrakhan collar, the first she had seen for years. He introduced the younger man as Dave.

She took them through the hall and their heads turned from side to side as they noticed the pictures on the wall. In the sitting-room they stood in the centre and looked around. The paintings were bathed in the light reflected from the snow outside.

"They're marvellous!" Helman exclaimed. "I've seen one or two Brents before, but never a whole roomful. What an impact they have!"

"I've had to rearrange them," said Dorothy. She had replaced the exhibition pictures with others from the studio, the walls had looked so bare. The replacements hung rather crookedly, too high or too low.

He moved closer to examine a picture.

"That's my mother, holding me in her arms," explained Dorothy.

"It's beautiful."

"Mummy never liked it. She said it was such an uncomfortable pose."

They went from picture to picture and she commented on the subjects: Dorothy and a friend paddling in the sea, in lemon and lime-green swim-suits, Dorothy sitting bareback on a donkey led by her mother, Mrs Brent painting in the studio with Dorothy as her model. "And look, there in the mirror, if you look closely, you can just see Daddy's face."

They admired everything and exclaimed with delight. They went from room to room, through the whole house. What marvels it contained, what a treasure chest it was!

"Would you like to see the studio?" asked Dorothy.

"You mean, there's more?" they asked incredulously.

They went outside, across the garden where a cold

wind was blowing from the sea, and down through the orchard. The early daffodils were smothered by the snow. Helman stepped carefully through the slush in his highly-polished shoes. The studio smelled damp and musty.

"It's just as he left it," she said.

There were paintings all round the wall, they were stacked on the floor. An unfinished canvas of the orchard in blossom stood on the easel.

The two men looked through the pictures, pausing over those they found most attractive: Dorothy carrying a tray laden with china, Dorothy and her mother picking blackberries, Mrs Brent and the housekeeper in the kitchen, the table heaped with vegetables.

Helman was on one knee by a stack of canvases. "Do you ever sell any?" he asked, without looking up.

"I've given them away, if anyone particularly liked them."

"Given them away!" exclaimed Dave.

"I did sell some of the larger ones. A man who owned a hotel asked me, and I thought it would be rather nice because in a hotel a lot of people would see them."

"How much did he pay you?"

"A hundred pounds, I think."

"A hundred pounds each?"

"Oh no, for the lot," she said. "It was some time ago."

"Do you know what they are worth now?" asked Helman.

"Not really," she said. Jeremy and Marilyn had never talked about money. "I suppose the exhibition will increase their value."

Helman stood up. "What will you do with them?" he asked.

"I don't know," she said.

They went back through the orchard, the branches of

the apple trees swaying and creaking in the wind. The sides of the valley were white with snow, and the sea at the end was the colour of slate. She left them in the sitting room, looking at the paintings and conferring together, while she went to make tea.

On her own in the kitchen, setting out the tray, she thought of his question. What *would* she do with them? The day would come when keeping the house would be too much for her. It was already a losing battle. If she moved to a bungalow there would be no room for the paintings. It was a problem to know what to do for the best. She made the tea and carried the tray into the room.

"It's the picture!" cried Helman as she entered. "It's the girl carrying the tray, it's the same one, isn't it?"

"I suppose it is," she said. "It's the same tray, anyway. I've changed a lot since then."

They assured her that they recognised her immediately. She placed the tray on the table and poured the tea.

"How extraordinary," said Helman, "to use the objects that Brent painted, to be surrounded by the world that he put into his pictures. It's a great privilege to be here."

"That's very kind of you."

"I wonder," he said slowly, as he drank his tea. "Do you have anyone to advise you?"

"No," she said.

He put down his cup and leaned forward, resting a hand on her arm. "Dorothy," he said, "I want you to promise me something."

She was rather taken aback, by the hand on her sleeve, by the use of her Christian name, by the idea that she should promise anything to a stranger. "What?" she asked.

"You have a very important collection," he said. "Once the exhibition has opened there'll be all sorts of people calling, auctioneers, dealers, collectors, all trying to persuade you to let them have your paintings. I want you to promise me that you won't sell any of them."

She was surprised. She had rather thought that he was a dealer. Perhaps she had been unfair to him, perhaps after all he simply liked her father's pictures.

"I'll remember what you say," she said.

They finished their tea and were preparing to go. He thanked her for allowing them to share the atmosphere of the Brent household. "We'll see you again at the opening?" he said.

"Oh, I'm not going."

"But you must!" he exclaimed. "You can't miss the opening."

"It's too far," she said. "I can't go there and back in a day."

"Surely the organisers expect you to be there."

"I'd have to stay overnight, there's no one I know."

"Be our guest," he said expansively. "We'll meet you at the station, go to the exhibition, take you out to dinner afterwards. We'll put you up in a hotel overnight. How would that be?"

For a moment Dorothy hesitated; she hardly knew the two men. They were waiting for an answer.

"I'd like to," she admitted.

"I'm delighted," he said. "We shall look forward to seeing you." He gave her his card. It read HELMAN AND STONE, *Fine Arts*, and had an address in the West End.

The train from Penzance arrived at Paddington in the late afternoon. She felt excited and a little anxious, as she walked down the platform, carrying her overnight bag. The young man was there to meet her and took her by taxi to the exhibition. How London had changed! There were tower blocks everywhere, and when she got out of the cab and looked around her, she thought she was amongst the sort of futuristic architecture that existed only in drawings and had not yet been built. There were tiers of flats with balconies, each stepped back behind the other, that made her think of the hanging gardens of Babylon. There were fountains splashing into pools. They entered an enormous foyer.

The gallery was already crowded with people standing in front of the brightly lit, glowing colours of the canvases. Helman came towards them, holding out his arms and embracing her. "My dear, have you met – ?" and he introduced her to so many people that she couldn't remember their names. "This is Brent's daughter," he would say. A press photographer took her photo in front of the girl on the swing of sixty years ago.

She tried to see the paintings, but there were so many people milling around that she could not get near. She caught snatches of conversation: "... bought at auction for five thousand... prices haven't reached their peak yet..."

He steered her away from the crowd into the bar. It was part of a huge conservatory where an indoor jungle grew several stories high; they stood on a balcony overlooking it and drank white wine. He introduced a young man who was making a radio programme about the school of painting. They arranged an interview at home.

She would have liked to go back to the gallery to speak to Jeremy and Marilyn, both of whom she had seen at a distance. But Helman and Dave whisked her away by taxi to a small, candle-lit restaurant. As they ate, he encouraged her to talk about Brent and his circle. She found that she had more stories than she had thought.

"Shall I tell you something?" she confided, towards the end of the meal. "I never really liked their work. I always thought it was rather old-fashioned."

"But you liked your father's?"

"Not all that much," she laughed.

The candle flame flickered low in its red glass bowl. He divided the rest of the bottle of wine between them, although Dorothy felt that she had already drunk too much, and with her permission lit a cigar.

He reproved her gently. It was a responsibility owning such a collection, he said. It she ever wanted to dispose of it, she had a duty to do what was best for the paintings and her father's reputation. "If you sent the whole lot to auction, they might make twenty-five thousand," he said. "And it would do nothing to enhance your father's name."

"So what should I do?"

The cigar smoke hung, blue in the air. "I'll make you an offer," he said. "I'll buy the whole studio, everything that's left, for fifty thousand pounds. I'll put on a Brent exhibition in the West End that will establish him as the leader of the group."

Fifty thousand pounds, she thought. It would buy a bungalow, it would free her from all her labour.

"You could keep a few as a memento."

She looked at his rosy face through the smoke and the candlelight. Her mind felt muzzy with the unaccustomed wine, with the unfamiliar setting and situation. It was a very tempting offer. But there was one thought that she had to cling to, that she must never forget.

"I'll have to think about it," she said.

"Of course," said Helman.

She felt indebted to him, but she knew that she must never get rid of the pictures, even if it meant more of a struggle as she got older.

Because if it wasn't for Daddy's painting, nobody would ever be interested in her, would they?

THE SALEROOM

an addiction

Sir *Alfred Munnings* PRA
Going to the Meet 1913
Oil on canvas 20¼ x 24¼ *in*
Signed, AJ Munnings
THE LAING ART GALLERY, NEWCASTLE UPON TYNE

A huntsman on a grey mare, silhouetted against the sky, is riding towards the viewer and the leading hounds are coming out of the picture.

The catalogues come in the post; two of them because I am on the auctioneer's mailing list and I have also put a small watercolour into the sale. It is Molly's weekend off and we have a catalogue each, abandoning everything else this Saturday morning to look them through.

"There's a Henry Scott Tuke, lot number eighty-three."

"And a Lamorna Birch, *Evening Sunlight on a Scottish River*. See illustration."

We both flick through to find the black and white reproduction.

"I've seen it before, it was in a sale a year or two ago. It's very dark, darker than the photograph, with an orange light on the trees."

"You can never tell from the photos."

There are quite a few familiar pictures. The two Charles Simpsons were in the last sale, they couldn't have sold. They should have a lower reserve this time.

"Oh, look at those two, lots three hundred and twenty-one and twenty-two. They're nice, who are they?"

"They look like Laura Knight."

"They're Harold Harvey! I expect they'll make a price, they're good subjects."

One shows children on a beach, a round-cheeked girl in a tam-o'-shanter and a boy pulling on a sock. In the other, fishermen are mending nets, with Newlyn harbour in the background.

It's a good sale, of more than average interest. There's a Stanhope Forbes and a Walter Langley and some of the St Ives artists.

"It's a pity, but we'll have to go to this one." When there's nothing interesting in a sale, there are no decisions, it's quite clear cut. There are temptations here.

We go to the preview. It's a cool, damp evening as we park on the seafront. "My god, it's *The Rain It Raineth Every Day*, it's Norman Garstin's picture." It really is; the light is pearly grey, there are reflections in the wet pavements. We hurry to the saleroom.

There are a lot of people in the doorway. I push my way through and start to look at the pictures, massed on the wall from floor to ceiling. It's difficult to take them in when they are crowded together like this, and then one catches my notice and I begin to see clearly. It is lot number eighty-three, a schooner at anchor. It is grey and misty, and unmistakably Henry Scott Tuke.

Once I am through the doorway, the two rooms seem less crowded. People are standing around, holding glasses of wine and chatting. I concentrate on the pictures until Molly joins me. "Look, there's Barry," she says. "I expect Barbara is somewhere around. Have you seen Stewart?"

We move around the corner into the second room. "Muriel," we exclaim. "Darlings," she says and Molly and Muriel kiss each other on the cheek. "How are you?"

As soon as I can I continue looking at the pictures. There's a lot of rubbish, as usual, a wall full of uninspired landscapes and seas. How could anyone have ever thought that they were worth producing? There's something very depressing about all this mediocrity crammed together. The artists were striving to produce something that had vision, that could delight the eye, that was fresh and bright. And instead they only managed a uniform dullness, shipping in rough seas, sunsets at Land's End, vases of flowers. How did they keep going? They must have known that their work was dead. Perhaps they hoped that one day, if they kept at it, they'd breathe some life into it.

If it's a poor sale, with nothing out of the ordinary, I begin to panic. I want to rush around as quickly as possible and leave. "But you haven't looked at anything yet," says Molly. "There's nothing here," I say. "How do you know?" she asks. "You haven't given it a chance." I feel stifled by the atmosphere of the saleroom. How tatty, how seedy it all is, how stale! I want to get out into the fresh air.

But today there is enough to lift the spirits. There's the schooner of Henry Scott Tuke, some cheerful St Ives pictures – a bright floral arrangement by Dorothea Sharp – a landscape, just a field and a hedge and a few ricks beneath a wide sky, by George Clausen. And the two Harold Harveys are superb, full of light and colour.

We move around the saleroom, every so often meeting Barry and Barbara again or Stew and Mew, as in a formal dance. When we encounter one of the other couples, we exchange a few remarks about the pictures we happen to be near.

"I can't stand that," says Barry of a modern naïve painting of a pot plant and a grapefruit on a striped tablecloth.

"I think it's rather charming," says Molly.

"I could have painted it myself."

We pass on until we come to Stew and Mew at a table of unframed prints and portfolios of etchings, the sort that Stewart is interested in.

"That's a nice one," says Molly, pointing to a nineteenth century watercolour on the wall behind them.

"Mmm ... yes," says Stew, too polite to contradict her but reserving his judgement.

"I'd give three hundred for that."

Everyone round about turns to see what it is that they have overlooked; perhaps there is something about it that they don't know. Molly cups her hand over Stewart's ear and whispers to him, "Roger's selling it."

"Good luck," says Stew.

On again, to ask for a Gotch sketch book to be brought out of safekeeping. The auctioneer's assistant has a bandaged hand; he has been bitten by a cat. "Have you had a tetanus injection?" asks Molly. I look at the fragile little sketchbook with its brown ink drawings of a century ago.

We take a glass of wine and stand in front of the two spotlit Harold Harveys. They are much more impressive than the photographs suggested.

"They're as good as any I've seen for sale," says Barry.

"Not quite the magic of his best."

"Not *quite*," he says. "But they're pretty good."

"Oh yes, they're pretty good."

We sip our wine and stare at them enviously.

"It's no good looking at those," says a dealer called Eric, who joins the group.

"What's the guide price?"

"Six to nine."

"Hundreds or thousands?" asks Molly ingenuously.

"Thousands, of course." He laughs. "It wouldn't surprise me if they make twenty thousand each."

Poor old Harvey! He was always hard up in his lifetime. He could have done with a share of the profit.

Molly and I have been all round. We put our heads together to confer, at a spot where a list of guide prices is conveniently to hand. "Well," she says. "Is there anything you fancy? Apart, that is, from the Harold Harveys."

"I wouldn't mind going for the Tuke."

"You're determined to get another Tuke, aren't you?"

"What do you think?"

"We've got enough boats. I like people, I like number ninety-four."

I haven't noticed it. I look through the catalogue and find Head of a Girl. "It's unsigned."

"I like it."

"But you don't know who painted it."

"Does that matter?"

"Yes, it does – at least from the financial point of view."

"But that's not why you buy pictures."

"No," I say. "But it enters into it."

We look up the estimates, two to three hundred each. We have about three hundred pounds, five hundred at most, that we could spend. We go back to look at the pictures again. There is no way of choosing between them.

"But it's unsigned," I say. "The Tuke is *right*."

"Stop talking like a dealer," says Molly. "You'll be saying it's a 'little cracker' next."

"Well, it is."

We go around the saleroom once more, pausing before our choices, trying to see them afresh. We consider bidding for them both, with a limit of two hundred and fifty on each; that way, we're not likely to get either. "To be sure of the Tuke, you'd have to go up to four or five hundred."

"All right," says Molly. "Go up to four hundred for the Tuke, and if you get it, that's it. But if you don't get it, I'll go up to four hundred for the girl."

It's too much for the portrait, but I agree; our plans are laid.

I take a last glance round. I meet Barry in the middle; we pause and look at each other. There's a feeling on both sides that we might be rivals. I know that he has quite a good Tuke collection.

"Well?" he says.

"Well?" I repeat.

"Are you coming on Thursday?"

"I think so. There are one or two we rather like. Are you coming?"

"Yes, there are one or two we like."

We grin at each other, both wondering furiously if we are interested in the same paintings. We seem to be making a slight circling movement around each other.

"It would be a shame to bid against you," I suggest.

"Yes," he agrees. "We must come to some arrangement, form a small ring."

"Is that legal?"

He shrugs, and continues to grin.

I come straight out with it. "I like the Tuke schooner." I pronounce the name 'Took' in my nervousness.

"It's a nice little painting," he says.

We pause.

"I'm mainly interested in something that comes up later on," he says. "I won't push the Tuke up too high."

"Good," I say.

We laugh, as though anything we have said has not been in deadly earnest, as though it was all pretence.

When the health service stopped paying overtime, the nurses had to take time off for any extra hours that they worked. Molly always has several days in hand and on Thursday comes to the sale.

"I thought we said we had finished," she says in the car. "I thought we weren't going to buy any more pictures."

"We could stop if we wanted to."

"That's what they always say."

"But we could."

"There's no room for any more, every bit of wall space is taken up. It seems ridiculous to stack them on the floor."

"We could sell a few."

"What's the point?"

"All right, we won't buy anything today."

Molly thinks for a while. "Do you want the Tuke?" she asks.

"Yes."

"Then try and get it. Go up to five hundred."

We drive along the cliffs. It is April weather, cold and windy and bright; the sea is a deep blue, with the purple shadows of clouds. The gorse is coming into flower and in the folds of the hills the catkins are pale yellow. St Ives shows up white in the distance.

We are in no hurry, not wanting to arrive for the start of the sale. When we go through the doors, the entrance hall is packed with people; from inside we hear the singsong voice of the auctioneer. We ease our way through. "What number has he reached?" whispers Molly; a young man points to the place on the catalogue that he is marking. The dealers seem to be younger at every sale.

"Lot number seventy-four," announces the auctioneer. "Nineteenth century lithograph, *Welsh Wedding, Running Away With the Bride*. What shall we say? Fifty pounds?"

He is much further on than we expect; he must be doing at least a hundred lots to the hour. He has nearly reached the Henry Scott Tuke and we are still in the hall. I like to have time to work myself into a good position when I am bidding. But the Tuke will be coming up in a few moments. I push into the doorway, but can get no further. The room beyond is crammed with people; above their heads I can just see the auctioneer sitting at a desk on top of a table, his back to the window.

"Lot number eighty-three, Henry Scott Tuke. *Schooner at Anchor*. What am I bid? Three hundred pounds? Two fifty then."

My heart begins to thump. I never come into the bidding at the start, I like to wait for it to get under way.

"Two eighty... three hundred... three twenty... three fifty... three eighty."

The bids rise rapidly, going up twenty or thirty pounds at a time. There is a pause at three hundred and eighty pounds. I raise my catalogue in the air, stretching my arm full length.

"Four hundred pounds in the doorway... four twenty... four fifty... four eighty."

I keep my hand raised throughout, to make sure that I don't lose his attention. I'd like to bid like those dealers who indicate their intentions with the slightest movement of the head or an eye muscle. But I want to make sure.

It has nearly reached my limit. More by luck than judgement, I have entered the bidding on the hundred, so that I can go out on my top bid.

"Five hundred pounds... five twenty." I have lowered my arm. "Five fifty?" asks the auctioneer. I shake my head and turn away, pushing past the smokers into the hall, my whole attitude expressing the belief that anyone who would pay a penny more than five hundred pounds for the watercolour must be mad. Behind me I hear the bidding take off again. "Five fifty I have over there... five eighty... six hundred pounds."

I give Molly a look of resignation, and hear the Tuke knocked down for eight hundred and fifty pounds. Inexorably the voice of the auctioneer grinds on with the next lot. I sit down beside Molly on the stairs. "Prices are high," she whispers. She has borrowed a catalogue from 'Sexton' Blake, a dealer we used to buy from, and is filling in some of the earlier prices on her own copy.

"That passed through my hands once," said Blake, pointing to the Tuke against which Molly is writing £850. "I think I sold it for seven quid."

Blake's conversation is always about pictures that now make thousands and which he sold for a few pounds. "Stanhope Forbeses, Harold Harveys, I couldn't get rid of them."

Soon afterwards my watercolour comes up for sale. I'm not a dealer, but I do sometimes buy a picture in order to sell it again, if it seems obviously underpriced. This is a Dutch painting of children on a beach, not one that I want to keep. I picked it up in an antique shop for sixty pounds. I've put a reserve of seventy-five on it, I'll be happy if it makes a small profit. I only do it for the fun.

It starts at fifty and soon goes up through the hundreds. To my surprise it continues through the two hundreds. Molly and I look at each other with raised eyebrows. "This one yours?" whispers Sexton Blake, quick to catch on. "Don't you recognise it?" asks Molly. "We bought it from you for seven quid." "No!" he exclaims, looking up to heaven. It passes three hundred; I feel slightly embarrassed, someone must be making an expensive mistake. It sells for three hundred and fifty pounds.

We breathe out together. Molly beckons me to put my ear close to her mouth. "I'll add that to my bid for the portrait," she says, the words tickling the inside of my ear. "I'll go up to eight hundred and fifty."

"No," I say, pulling away. "It's not worth it."

"Lot one hundred and twenty-nine, the head of a girl.

Fifty pounds.... Forty then. Forty I've got... fifty... eighty... one hundred pounds."

It sticks at one hundred and twenty and seems about to be knocked down to a dealer standing in the doorway.

"YES," shouts Molly.

"One hundred and twenty from outside... one fifty... one eighty." "YES." "Two hundred... two twenty." "YES." "Two fifty... two eighty." "YES." "Three hundred... three twenty." "YES." "Three fifty..."

"Stop it, Molly," I urge. "That's all our profit from the watercolour gone."

But she doesn't hear me. She is standing up on the stairs and leaning over the banisters. "YES," she shouts at regular intervals.

"No," I say, tugging at her sleeve. "Don't go any higher." She brushes me away.

"Five hundred pounds... five twenty." "YES." "Five fifty... five eighty."

The dealer in the doorway turns round to stare at Molly, animosity in his glance. "YES," shouts Molly.

"Six hundred pounds," calls the auctioneer. Although the sum involved is not huge, there is a tension in the air. There is a sense of battle and the audience is hushed, listening intently, as they usually are only if thousands of pounds are at stake. The auctioneer, responding to the mood, raises the increment. "Six fifty." "YES." "Seven hundred... seven fifty." "YES."

No, no, no. Stop it Molly, please. That's enough.

"Eight hundred pounds... eight fifty." "YES." "Nine hundred pounds." The auctioneer tries to raise the increment to a hundred pounds a time. "One thousand pounds."

"NO." Molly sits down on the stairs and I sigh with relief. My shirt is sticking to me and I pluck it away from my chest. "Thank goodness," I say.

"At nine hundred pounds..." The auctioneer looks around the room, then brings down the gavel or whatever it is that he uses to make a sharp rap. "Sold."

There's a murmur in the crowd, as the tension eases and the questions begin. The picture was only expected to make two hundred at most. The dealer who bought it looks back angrily at Molly.

"Shall we go now?" I ask. We have nothing to collect after the sale, but we decide to wait and see the Harold Harveys sold. The tension builds up again, the auctioneer's assistant is taking bids on the phone. We are linked with the art world of London, perhaps even New York. *Fishermen Mending Nets* starts at five thousand and sells at sixteen. *Children On The Beach* reaches the same price. They are not record prices for Harvey and there is very little drama.

We leave before the end. As we are going to the door we meet Barry. He is delighted; he has bought the St Ives seascape that he wanted. Away from the others, in the bright light of the entrance, it looks superb. It's a good buy and it emphasises our empty-handedness.

Stewart joins us on the steps, carrying a stack of etchings. He too is grinning. "You knew about the Laura Knight," he says in a voice that sounds accusing, with more than a hint of admiration in it.

"No," we say innocently.

"The portrait of the girl that made nine hundred pounds. Apparently it's by Laura Knight, it can be authenticated. The dealer who bought it hoped to get it for a couple of hundred."

"I shouldn't feel sorry for him," says Barry. "He'll still do very well out of it."

"Did you recognise it?" asks Stewart.

"Well –" I try to look modest, without saying any more.

"I knew it was good," says Molly.

We feel a bit flat going home in the empty estate car. We had nearly had a Tuke, we had nearly had a Laura Knight, and we are returning from the chase without anything. The way to enjoy auctions is either to decide that there is nothing you want, and stay away. Or else to go all out for something that you really want, and make sure that you carry it off like a trophy afterwards. Otherwise you feel very low.

"Never mind," says Molly. "You did very well on the Dutch watercolour."

"That's true," I say. I am nearly three hundred pounds better off. I'd have to write several articles to earn that.

6
A PICTURE OF PROFIT
from the financial pages...

Dame Laura Knight RA
Wind and Sun
Watercolour, 38 x 44 in
Provenance: *sold at Sotheby's in May 1985*

This atmospheric scene of two young women on the cliff top with rugs, a deckchair and a parasol, held the world record of £60,000 for a Newlyn School painting for two months, until beaten in July 1985 by Stanhope Forbes's Business Slack in the Village – Boys Playing Tops, *sold for £63,800.*

The closest thing to a Stock Exchange 'big bang' is occurring in the art market. In the past five years the value of modern British paintings has increased 1000 per cent.

At the top end of the market are the pictures of the Newlyn School. The world probably woke up to their charms after the two exhibitions *Artists of the Newlyn School 1880-1900* and *Painting in Newlyn 1900-1930*, and the combined exhibition at the Barbican. Another landmark was Phillips' sale in London of pictures from the Queen's Hotel, Penzance. This was the first time a major collection of Newlyn School works had come under the hammer. Harold Harvey's *The Pedlar* was bought for £45,000 by art-dealer Richard Green, said to have the best eye in the business for a commercially saleable picture. It could well fetch double the figure now.

The enormous success of that sale brought hundreds of pictures off the walls of private houses in the West Country.

"The sheer quantity coming to light is amazing," says a Phillips spokesman. "Little old ladies whose parents perhaps bought a painting on holiday in Cornwall which has been hanging on their wall for years are coming in to find out more, or put them into a sale. One client this year brought in two pictures by Harold Harvey and asked, 'Have you heard of him?' She thought they might be worth £100. We put a reserve of £15,000 for the two – she couldn't believe it. In the event, we got £12,000 for one and she decided to keep the other." Harold Harvey is the current top-seller of the second generation of Newlyn artists.

The sensational rise in prices is due to the fall in the value of money and the scarcity of fine pictures. The prices of Continental Post-Impressionists have risen beyond the means of all except the mega-rich. In comparison, the British School is relatively undervalued, even cheap. Some experts feel that prices for Newlyn School pictures have peaked, or nearly so, and that the works of the Forbeses and the Knights, of Harold Harvey and the others have for the time being seen the large gains. They point to the way that the art market is cyclical, that its trends come and go. But dealers such as Richard Green think there is still plenty of 'fresh' work around (pictures not seen in the saleroom for the last ten years). Adds Francis Farmer of Christie's: "We believe there's still quite a bit of mileage left." Nowhere else in the art scene is the mood so bullish.

The boom may also be ascribed to an increase in the public's awareness of art. People are buying what they like, not what they feel they ought to like. Taste has swung away from the heavy, sentimental Victorian art, to the cleaner, sunnier and more everyday tastes of Post-Impressionism. And where once only Whistler, Wilson Steer, Sickert and the Camden Town School raised a flicker of interest, now a host of other British Impressionists and Post-Impressionist painters are being revalued. In the process, many received opinions have been burst open. Modern British art history has had to be rewritten.

In 1974 art dealer David Messum organised A *Breath of Fresh Air*, the first commercial exhibition devoted to the Newlyn School for forty years. He had come across the paintings while scouring the West Country for pictures to include in his 1969 exhibition *The Devonshire Scene*. "They were so full of colour and light," he says, "so refreshing and different from the Victorian paintings then in vogue I felt they should be put on the map."

This the Newlyn School undoubtedly is. In Messum's exhibition a Norman Garstin picture sold for £450 – now they sell for anything upwards of £20,000. The most expensive Stanhope Forbes was priced at £2,000. Today an important painting by Stanhope Forbes can fetch from £20,000 to £80,000. On the very day that the Newlyn School exhibition opened at the Barbican, Forbes's *Business Slack in the Village – Boys Playing Tops*, dated 1888, was sold for a world record £63,000 at Lawrence Fine Art, Crewkerne, Somerset. It had come for sale from a woman who lives near Sherborne and whose family had owned it for fifty years. Alerted that it might make a lot of money, she had instructed the auctioneer, "Don't phone me in case it is bad news." Lawrence's had estimated only £6,000 to £10,000 for the picture. It was bought by a London dealer. Business is far from slack in the village of Newlyn!

Peyton Skipwith of the Fine Art Society recalls paying in 1969 what was a high price at the time for Elizabeth Forbes's *A Game of Old Maid* and selling it for £1,100. "I think the buyer has earned more in royalties from the picture postcard printed since than she paid for the picture," he says. At today's values, it would be worth up to £100,000.

But the £100,000 barrier has yet to be broken. A classic Newlyn School painting by Harold Knight to be sold later this year could be the first picture of the school to reach six figures.

Or it could be a painting by his wife, Dame Laura. A few years ago, it was a struggle for a major work by Laura Knight to reach £4,000. In recent sales her best paintings have realised anything from £12,000 to the record £60,000 at Sotheby's for a watercolour, *Wind and Sun*.

Who will be the first to break through the £100,000 barrier? At the moment Stanhope Forbes is in the lead with Laura Knight a close second. Harold Knight is strongly favoured, and Harold Harvey is well up-front. If the right picture comes to auction, it could be Elizabeth Forbes, or an outsider like Garstin, Tuke or Gotch. Whoever it is, the day cannot be far off. Big bang indeed!

....and from the media pages

Stanhope Alexander Forbes RA
A Fish Sale on a Cornish Beach
Oil on canvas, 47 3/4 x 61 *in*
Signed and dated STANHOPE A FORBES 1885
Exhibited: Royal Academy, 1885
CITY MUSEUM AND ART GALLERY, PLYMOUTH

On a wet beach in a cool, pearly light, a fisherman stands with two women, the fish for sale lying on the sand at their feet. Behind them the seashore is crowded with men and women loading baskets and a cart, while the rest of the catch is being brought ashore from the fishing fleet whose tan sails are strung along the high horizon.

In a classic exchange of the American cinema, two men pass in the street in Victorian London. "Good morning, Mr Dickens," says one. "Good morning, Mr Thackeray," says the other.

The same device is used in Television South-West's drama documentary about the artists of the Newlyn School, *A Breath of Fresh Air*. The characters spend much of their time telling each other who they are. Stanhope Forbes turns the corner of a lane and bumps into Frank Bramley. "Frank Bramley!" he exclaims. "Stanhope Forbes!" exclaims Frank Bramley. "What are you doing here?"

Later, Stanhope Forbes and Walter Langley march from opposite ends across the beach at Porthcurno and meet in the middle. "I'm Walter Langley, the watercolourist," says Walter Langley, in a comic Midlands accent to show that he comes from Birmingham. "I've been wanting to meet you," says Stanhope Forbes. "I've heard a lot about you."

But having met, they have nothing to say to each other. They set to work in front of their easels. Stanhope Forbes has finished painting A *Fish Sale on a Cornish Beach*, and obviously disappointed and puzzled by the way it has shrunk to about a third of its original size, he turns to painting young girls. He does this quite literally, dabbing red paint on the end of his model's nose with his square-ended brush (a nice touch of authenticity, this, as it cleverly introduces the Newlyner's notorious square-brush technique). When it happens a second time, and once more a sequence ends with a little girl running away after having had her nose daubed with paint, you wonder if the film is trying to say something about Stanhope's fixations. Or have they got him mixed up with Lewis Carroll?

"There's Thomas Cooper Gotch!" exclaims Forbes, as he passes by the end of a Newlyn alleyway that has been brightened up with pots of geraniums and obviously expects the visit of a film crew at any moment. And Thomas Cooper Gotch is at it too! He doesn't look up, he is busy spreading gold paint over a spray of leaves held by a child in a doorway. This must be a reference to *The Golden Dream*, for which Gotch had the leaves and fruit of an apple tree specially gilded, but what the film seems to be leading towards is the great day when the Newlyn artists discover that they can actually put paint on to canvas.

But no such dramatic climax arrives. The film introduces some of the local inhabitants. Three yokels sit on the quayside watching Stanhope Forbes at work, grinning and nudging each other. He offers them fourpence to pose for him. "For saxpence oi'd dance for 'ee!" says the yokel, breaking into a lumbering hornpipe.

There's a Mr Plummer leaning on his garden gate as Stanhope and Elizabeth come down the road. For some reason his name is insisted upon. "Here's Mr Plummer, my dear." "Good morning, Mr Plummer," says Elizabeth. "Folk do say you two be gettin' wed," says Mr Plummer, whose name perhaps has something to do with his mummerset accent. "Folk do say more than they know," says Elizabeth, putting him down sharply. Mr Plummer's face registers confusion.

At about this point in the film you begin to wonder how the director is going to introduce a life-class scene. It is one of the rules of films of this sort, if not their raison d'être, that there has to be at least one scene with a nude model. And the artists of the Newlyn School believed in painting ordinary people going about their ordinary lives, especially in the open air.

There is no need to worry. The passing of time, we are told, brings many changes to Newlyn. We see fingers reaching lasciviously to pluck grapes from a bowl of fruit at a twilit party, with red lanterns in the trees and jazz music in the background. We know what the morals of the new generation are like.

On the rocks a nude figure stares out to sea, some flimsy material flowing in the breeze behind her in the manner of Isadora Duncan. Another girl sits naked at her feet. They hold the pose for the required length of time, or perhaps a little longer.

The film ends with the auction of one of Stanhope Forbes's least inspired paintings, a portrait of an elderly musician. It has been around the salerooms without reaching its reserve for quite a while. It is knocked down, as they say in the trade, for two thousand pounds. Whether this is meant to illustrate the triumph of the Newlyn School, or whether it is just terribly sad, is not at all clear.

7
THE DEALER

talking pictures

Ernest Procter
Newlyn
Oil on canvas
Provenance: *The Government Art Collection*
MOLLY AND ROGER TREVAIL

The simplified shapes of a Procter painting make houses and boats look like models, and Newlyn like a toy-town beside the sea.

Eric rings out of the blue on Sunday morning, prompted perhaps by our brief encounter at the preview to the sale. He is very apologetic, he knows it is short notice but could he possibly come and see our pictures this afternoon? I'd be delighted. I love showing off our collection, especially to someone as discerning as Eric. I give complicated directions on how to find the house.

He has been promising to come for a long time, ever since we visited his gallery. There was nothing much that we liked, but we talked of pictures and eventually he closed the shop and we went to his house to see his collection. It was very enviable, especially the Birches and the Tukes.

The house is tidy, there are no children at home to throw it into disarray. I light the fire, and we wait for him to find his way through the lanes to the valley.

There's a knock on the door, earlier than expected; the dog goes frantic. Molly calms her while I let Eric in. He is puffy, unhealthy-looking, fortyish. He found the house without any trouble. It's a shame the weather is still so cold and damp.

We start straightaway on the pictures. It is a dull day and the light is not very good. We try the electric but decide that natural light is better. I don't like picture lights; the pictures beneath them remain constant. I like to see them change at different times of the day or at different seasons of the year. On a summer's morning with the door open, the sunlight slants on to the Ernest Procter and it becomes a different picture.

It's a view of Newlyn that we were lucky to acquire; it came from the Government Art Collection, used for furnishing state offices. There's a label on the back saying that it is not to be removed from room 246 at Somerset House. The surface was covered with what we thought was brown varnish; we realised later that it was furniture polish. For fifty years the charladies at Somerset House had given it a daily wipe over with their polishing dusters. When we had it cleaned it came up beautifully, so fresh and colourful... This one came from the same collection, only it hung in British embassies in the Caribbean: cool water meadows, with distant hills. You can imagine how evocative it was of England, in some hot, foreign clime...

"How did they come into your possession?" asks Eric.

"Aha!" we say mysteriously. No dealer ever says how he obtained a picture, unless he knows you can find out anyway.

Every picture has its story, stories about the subject matter and stories about its acquisition. How we picked up this one in a junk shop for twenty quid because we liked it, and when it was cleaned the initials D.S. showed up clearly in the bottom left-hand corner. It was a Dorothea Sharp.

"Hasn't she taken off recently!" says Eric. "Two thousand for her little beach scenes, three or four thousand for her flower paintings."

How we bid for a Tuke, unsuccessfully, at an up-country auction and a saleroom porter came across and very secretively passed me a note: 'If you are interested in Tuke I have a nice example of his work.' It gave the number of a car, and we met in the car park afterwards. The dealer opened up the back of the estate and uncovered the painting. It was a beauty, a boy hauling on a rope, but I didn't dare buy it because it was in a car park and the price was too reasonable. I've always regretted it.

How we bought at auction the Charles Simpson painting of children on the beach, and were immediately offered a profit on it, before it left the saleroom.

How in a small house-sale I hoped to buy a Fred Evans cheaply, but a picture dealer had spotted it. We battled it out in bids that rose by five pounds a time, all the way from a hundred to seven hundred pounds.

"We thought we'd paid too much for it," says Molly.

"You could double that now," says Eric.

Stories of the chase, stories of the ones that got away and the ones that were caught. It takes two hours to go around the whole house, which is about normal for the course. Two hours of lovely picture talk. How delightful for the enthusiast, how boring for anyone else!

Then we sit down by the fire. I feel that I have talked too much, that I have put my own pleasure first in showing (off) the pictures. "It becomes an obsession," I say apologetically.

"Oh yes," Eric agrees. "You feel that there's a picture you've got to have, and then once you've got it, it doesn't seem to matter so much."

"Is that how you can sell them?"

"There are some that I could never sell, my Tukes, for example. But they tie up all my capital. That's the money I should be trading with, but I could never release it so I'm always poor."

"Do you sell many pictures – or 'shift' them, as they say?"

"I live by it, I sell enough to be registered for VAT. But I only buy what I like, I buy for myself really. And then when I've lived with a picture for a while I begin to see faults in it, the proportion of a figure looks wrong, or a hand seems to have been painted in by someone else, and from then onwards I can only see the fault, it blots out everything else."

"It sounds like being married," says Molly.

"Then I want to get rid of it as quickly as possible, I'll accept anything as long as I get my money back. I never make more than ten per cent on a painting."

"Ten per cent!" I say. "If I was a dealer, I'd expect more than that."

"Most of them mark up about fifty per cent."

"I would have thought a hundred more likely."

"It's not really worth my while, with the petrol and time. Last week I went to a house sale that was advertised in a local paper, pictures by Stanhope Forbes and Walter Langley. When I got there, they were prints. A complete waste of a day. And I'm badly placed where I live, it's too out of the way. If you're going to deal, you need to be on a main road, and in an area where there's some wealth."

"Roger always dreams of being a dealer," says Molly.

"Oh no, not really," I say, very embarrassed.

"You do."

"Well, I fantasise a bit sometimes," I admit. "But I'm sure I wouldn't want to be really."

"You are already, at heart," says Molly. "If you can make ten pounds on a picture, you're delighted. It means more to you than being paid for a story."

"Oh no, that's not true."

"When Sexton Blake offered you those three ship paintings for a hundred and forty pounds, you were thrilled. You were trembling so much you could hardly write the cheque out. You couldn't wait."

"No, Molly, please."

"There are a lot of forgeries around of nineteenth century ship portraits," says Eric gloomily. "There's a man in Bristol producing them. I think I've bought one. I gave two hundred pounds for it in Plymouth."

"That's probably what Sexton sold you, Roger."

"No, they were by the Falmouth fisherman-painter, Jack West. I don't think Sexton recognised them."

"Then you couldn't sleep all night for worrying. You woke me up at two in the morning to make me promise not to let you ever do it again. You were carried away, you said."

"They were 'right', though. I sold them to another dealer for a hundred pounds each."

"And then you couldn't sleep worrying that you had cheated someone and that Sexton Blake had probably picked them up from some poor old lady for a song."

"I can't sleep at all before a sale," says Eric. "I worry about every picture I buy and every picture I sell."

"What do you worry about?"

"I worry that I'm paying too much for it, or that I'm selling it too cheaply and ought to hold on to it. I bought a Harvey once for seventeen pounds and sold it for twenty-four. Then I bought it back for eleven hundred and sold it for twelve-fifty. If I bought it back again I'd have to give five thousand for it. I'd have done better to keep it in the first place."

"It seems to me you take your pleasures sadly," says Molly. "Why do you do it?"

"I can't do anything else. I can't paint, I can't write. I

feel envious of Roger, when I see those rows of books that he has written. It must be wonderful to have created all that."

"It's nothing much," I say modestly, shifting uneasily.

"I can't create anything," says Eric. "So I deal. But I can't even do that very well. I never pick up a bargain, I always have to pay top prices for any pictures I buy, because they are pictures I like, and I sell them for a little bit more."

"Sexton Blake always says he's waiting for 'the big one', the picture bought for a pound in a jumble sale that turns out to be an old master worth millions."

"He's out ten, twelve hours a day, hunting for it. It's not worth it."

"It's his life."

"He'll never find it."

"But it keeps him going. It's the search that matters."

We fall silent, staring into the fire, and Molly goes to make some tea. I start telling the story of the bookseller and the American, and begin all over again when Molly comes back with the tea-things on a tray.

A bookseller sold a rare volume to an American collector for one thousand pounds and fifty pence. The American wrote out the cheque, and then asked as a matter of interest how the bookseller had arrived at such an odd price.

"Oh, that's easy," said the bookseller. "I've always wanted to make a clear thousand pounds profit on a single book."

I laugh hysterically, I don't know why I am so amused by the story. I have strongly ambivalent feelings towards the dealer, I despise and admire him, both at the same time. The others are hardly affected by the story at all.

Molly turns to Eric. "Which picture fills you with envy?" she asks. "Which would you like most? Which will you take home with you?"

"I like the Simpson, the girls on the beach."

"It's my favourite," she agrees.

"I think I could live without it," I say.

"I thought you liked it."

"Yes, but if I parted with any of them, that's the one I should miss least."

"Do you want to sell it?" asks Eric.

"Well..." I hesitate. "I suppose if I had an offer I couldn't refuse..."

"What would that be?"

"I wouldn't consider anything under five thousand."

"Mm."

"And I suppose seven and a half might be pushing it a bit... Somewhere within that range."

"Are you serious?"

"Of course he's not," says Molly. "He's just playing with the idea, he's pretending to be a dealer again. It's half mine, and I wouldn't dream of selling it."

"Not at the right price?"

"Not at any price."

"If you ever do want to sell it," says Eric, "just give me a ring."

8
THE SANDPIT

Jennifer Rowe's story

Charles Simpson RI
On Porthminster Beach, St Ives
Oil on canvas, 30 x 40 in
Signed, Charles Simpson
Exhibited: New Bond Street, London, 1917
MOLLY AND ROGER TREVAIL

The girl on the beach phones to say that she would like to come and see her picture. We made contact with her after the auction at which we bought it; the auctioneer forwarded our letter to the lady who sold it and whom he believed to be the girl in the painting. She replied, confirming that it was her portrait and saying that she would be happy to tell us all she remembered. Time passed and we thought it unlikely that she would do anything about it, until her unexpected call.

Although she must be nearly eighty, she is driving down from Devon. She is arriving for coffee at eleven o'clock. I stand in the road, to make sure that she finds the house. It is a bright spring day; the branches of the trees are bare against a blue sky. The bank is full of primroses and daffodils.

She arrives in a very well-maintained car that must be quite twenty years old. She backs it neatly into the parking space and with a little bit of a struggle gets out of the driving seat. She is tall, white-haired, and wears a cream-coloured suit. We walk up the steep drive to the house.

In the sitting-room she stands and looks at her picture. Three children are playing on the sand, with the waves breaking behind them. They have dug a pit and wait for the tide to fill it.

It seems like a pretty, summery scene and yet there are tensions within it. The girl on the left sits with her legs in the sandpit. She wears a knitted stocking cap in dark green with a matching cardigan over a short pink dress.

She is very distinct from the two girls on the right, who sit low in the sand. One has golden-brown hair tied with a pink ribbon; she wears a shiny white dress and is filling a red bucket with sand. The other looks slightly disgruntled; she sits with her hands folded in her lap and wears a blue dress and a straw sunbonnet. They merge with the natural colours of the breaking waves and the sand, but the girl on her own stands out in her striking, almost harsh, green and softer pink.

The composition also emphasises the differences between them. The group seems to tilt to the right, with the pair almost falling out of the picture. As they sink, the girl in the green cardigan appears to be rising.

She looks at them but they do not look at her. They are worlds apart. She is twentieth century and modern; they are Victorian and old-fashioned.

There is a class difference too. She doesn't seem to know these children. She looks in her smart clothes as though she is from up-country. They are local and belong to the beach more than she does.

Where has she come from?

I look at the old lady and wait for an answer. I wonder what she is thinking as she sees herself as she was seventy years ago. An old photograph only emphasises the passing of time. But the morning of the painting is present now, in all its immediacy. There seems little connection between the white-haired old lady and the girl on the beach, nothing to suggest that they are the same person.

After staring at the painting for a long time, she begins to tell her story. "I am the girl in the green stocking cap. I was Jennifer Rowe then, and I lived with my parents in London. They came from a Cornish family and when the zeppelins were bombing London during the first world war, my mother brought me down to St Ives, to stay with her aunt in one of the coastguard cottages above Porthminster beach."

"That would have been in the summer of 1916," I say.

"It could well have been. At the beginning of September the local schools opened again after the summer holidays and suddenly the beaches were empty. I went to play on Porthminster beach as usual and there were only two other girls there. They, too, lived in the coastguard cottages, though I don't know why they were not at school. The attendance officer called on my mother soon afterwards, but before anything could be done about it we went back to London as the raids had stopped. As we were the only three children on the beach we played together, though I didn't know their names. We dug a large hole in the sand and waited for the tide to come in and fill it. After a while Mr Simpson walked along the beach, though I did not know who he was until later. He wore a blue suit, he had been invalided out of the army."

"I don't think so, he never served in the army."

"That was what I understood."

"He was expected to have an army career like his father, who was a major-general. But he was injured in a riding accident and became a painter instead."

"I'm sure he was wearing blue, which made me think he was a wounded soldier."

"Perhaps that was the impression he wanted to create."

"He was carrying a sketching pad and he made some sketches of us, though during the war it was illegal to sketch out of doors. Later he asked my mother if I could go to his studio. It was overlooking the harbour and I went several times. Sometimes he gave me half a crown, but not always. He did three paintings of me; in another I'm sitting on top of a sandcastle, in the same clothes. I was very proud of the green stocking cap and cardigan. They were amongst the first machine-knitted garments in the country; my uncle had recently set up a factory in London to produce them. I also had a doll dressed in the same cap and cardigan; he gave them away as an advertisement. I loved wearing the green with a pink dress and it's a combination, pink and green, that I've favoured all my life. I didn't like my hair in the picture. I'd just come out of the sea and it was still wet. Normally it was quite curly and I didn't think he should have shown it in rats' tails. Later on the pictures were exhibited in New Bond Street. My mother received an invitation to the preview, but I didn't go. She didn't buy any of the paintings, I don't think she even considered it. It was thirty-five years before I saw the picture again."

She pauses for me to register the strangeness of her story.

"I grew up and married and went to live in the north of England. Just before our twentieth wedding anniversary we came to Cornwall on holiday. My husband wanted to give me a special anniversary present, so I said let's see if Charles Simpson is still living in Cornwall and if he is perhaps we could buy one of his paintings."

"He left Cornwall for a time. He lived in London, but was back in the thirties."

"This would have been in 1951. We found that he had a studio in Penzance. We went along, not knowing at all what to expect. A maid answered the door."

"A maid? I don't think they had a maid. Are you sure it wasn't Ruth Simpson?"

"I'm sure she was a maid, she was dressed in black with a maid's cap on her head. We were ushered in and Mr Simpson came down from his studio. 'How extraordinary!' he kept saying. 'How extraordinary!' Because that very day he was sending off an exhibition to Bolton in Lancashire and he had just finished packing the picture of me on the beach. 'How extraordinary,' he said, 'after all these years!' If we had gone a day later we would have missed it. We had to buy it after that."

Molly rushes in between patients and while Jennifer Rowe tells her story again I make the coffee. From the kitchen I can hear her voice; she takes pleasure in imitating Charles Simpson's pronunciation, the long middle vowel of 'how extraordinary'. It seems as though he is in the next room.

"How could you bear to part with it?" asks Molly. It is incomprehensible to me, with all its personal associations. I am only afraid that seeing it again she may feel that she can't live without it, and ask for it back.

"I don't mind at all, dear," she says. "My husband died, I married again and was widowed a second time. I moved into a smaller house and needed the money for redecorating. I'm very glad for you to have it."

As she leaves, she eases herself backwards into the driver's seat, to swing her legs into the car. Her skirt rises a few inches above her knees and for a second she is recognisable as the girl Charles Simpson painted seventy years ago at the edge of the sandpit on Porthminster Beach.

9

A LOST PAINTING

the rediscovery

Henry Scott Tuke RA
The Diver
Oil on canvas, 50 x 70 in
Signed and dated HS TUKE 1898
Exhibited: Royal Academy 1899, Liverpool 1899,
  Oldham 1900, Pittsburgh 1901
Illustrated: Magazine of Art 1899; frontispiece

"I went to see Mrs Hooper today," says Molly.

I look up sharply. "Yes."

"She's very poorly. She's full of fluid, she could hardly breathe."

"Did you – ?"

"She's on water tablets now, she'll pull through all right."

"Did you go inside the house?"

"Of course I went inside."

"What was it like?"

"Dark and gloomy, you couldn't see much. I didn't want to open it all up on my first visit."

I can't wait any longer. "Did you see the Tuke?" I ask.

"There were lots of pictures around, but I didn't have time to look at them... She was too unwell, she could hardly talk... But I did discover something. She's not Mrs Hooper at all, she's Miss Hooper."

"Really?"

"Denzil Hooper was her brother."

"That makes sense, her name couldn't be Hooper if she had married. But who's the man she lives with?"

"He's called Barker. He kept saying 'Miss Hooper', so I said 'Who are you then?' and he said 'Mr Barker'. That's what they call each other, Miss Hooper and Mr Barker."

"What's he doing there?"

"He explained to me before I left. He used to be the gardener and handyman and then he moved into the house after her brother's death. He now does everything for her, shops, cooks, washes her clothes. But they remain very formal, Miss Hooper and Mr Barker."

"That's strange."

"It's not all that unusual, I know of other elderly couples. Sometimes there's a lodger and the husband dies and the lodger stays on with the wife."

"It must be the Denzil Hooper who bought the Tuke, it's got to be... Are you going back again?"

"I shall be going daily for a while, the old man needs some help. He's not much fitter than she is, really."

"Find out if she's still got the beach study."

"She's got it, she's quite sure she has. She's a bit senile, but she was quite clear today. She's very much better, the swelling in her legs has gone down a lot. She remembered the name when I asked her. 'Tuke, he lived at Falmouth, didn't he?' Her brother admired him greatly. She was sure he had the beach study, she'd get Mr Barker to look it out.

"She was charming. She's got this reputation in the village of being a recluse, but she's not at all like that. She was very gracious, a touch of the grand lady about her. I asked if I could pull the curtains back and she said, 'Of course, dear, do as you like.' I pulled them back and the sunlight streamed into the room. You'll never believe this, I could have died! The beach study is nothing compared to it."

"What is it?"

"On the end wall is one of Tuke's bathing scenes!"

"Really?"

"It's just like one of the famous ones, *August Blue* or the one with all the colours, what is it called?"

"*Ruby, Gold and Malachite.*"

"That's it, it's just like that, with half a dozen boys swimming from a boat."

"It's not a print, is it?"

"Of course it's not, I know a print when I see one."

"How big is it?"

"It's enormous, it dominates the room." She stretches both arms as far as possible. "As big as that," she says. It must be six feet wide.

"Good heavens!" I say.

"It's very powerful, I've never seen anything like it in a private house."

"Has it got a name on it?"

"Only the signature."

"Is it dated?"

"I don't remember the date, I couldn't spend too long looking at it."

"I wonder which one it is. It must be in the registers, it sounds like a major work."

"And that's not all," says Molly. "There are more in the same room, portraits and watercolours of ships. Heaven knows what's in the rest of the house! I said, 'Miss Hooper, my husband would love to see your paintings,' and she said, 'Bring him along, dear. I'd be happy to meet him.'"

"Oh Molly!"

I look up the Tuke registers before going to see the

painting, but there is not enough information to identify it. I turn over the pages, thinking that it must be there somewhere among the twelve hundred entries. But which one is it? All the important large paintings belong to public collections. *Noonday Heat* is in the Tuke collection of the Royal Cornwall Polytechnic Society. *August Blue* belongs to the Tate. *Ruby, Gold and Malachite* is loaned to various City of London institutions, but belongs to the Guildhall.

With half a dozen boys bathing from a boat, this is the painting it most resembles. I read in a note in the register that it seems to have been frequently copied, including the signature. A copy was sold as an original in Plymouth in the early nineteen seventies, the buyer eventually obtaining a refund from the gallery.

I try to convince myself that Denzil Hooper's painting will turn out to be another copy.

"She could be quite different today," says Molly, as she parks her nurses' car under the high stone wall of the house. She is still in uniform, having left Miss Hooper for her last call of the day; she has picked me up on the way. "We'll just have to see what she's like. If she's difficult, you'll have to slip away quietly."

I feel nervous as I unlatch the tall iron gates, which creak open. We pass through; in front of the house is a circular lawn, with a gravel drive sweeping around both sides to the porch. There are laurel and rhododendron bushes between the drive and the walls. The front of the house is covered with ivy; at the side are some pine trees, higher than the roof and sighing in the wind.

Our feet crunch on the gravel. I follow Molly round to a side door, which she opens without knocking. "Hullo," she calls. "It's only me."

I feel like an intruder in the kitchen, with its cream-painted cabinets, its row of brown-leafed geraniums on the window shelf. It smells of stale meals and cats. Molly has gone through another door into a dark hallway. "Come on," she says, as I am hanging back. "Follow me."

I follow through the darkness and then she opens a door; there's a little more light in the room beyond. I can see two figures, each wrapped in a rug, sitting on either side of an electric fire. The old lady has a cat on her lap.

"Hullo, Miss Hooper, dear," calls Molly. "How are you today?" She kneels beside her and takes her hands. "Ooh, your hands are cold, aren't they?"

I stand just inside the doorway. The pictures around the room are merely dark shapes. Mr Barker is struggling to move aside his rug and stand up.

"No, don't get up," says Molly. "This is my husband, I said I'd bring him along."

I move forward and shake hands with Miss Hooper; her hand is like ice. "How kind of you to come," she says. I shake hands with Mr Barker.

They haven't put down any books or turned off the radio; they weren't doing anything when we arrived, they were just sitting there, waiting. The room smells of drying urine.

"Shall I pull back the curtains?" asks Molly.

"We always keep them drawn because of the draught," says Miss Hooper. "And Denzil always liked to keep the light off the watercolours. He used to be running up and down stairs all day long, closing the curtains as the sun moved round the house."

"He sounds just like Roger," says Molly.

She starts pulling back the curtains in the large bay window and the cat jumps to the floor at the noise. The intense spring sunlight floods the room, drowning the electric light of the small table-lamp by which they have been sitting.

The picture on the end wall springs to life.

There they are, in startling presence. I can see at once that it is not *Ruby, Gold and Malachite*. There are one, two, three, four, *five* boys, three in a boat with a small mizzen sail and two on the rocks. One of them is about to dive into the water. It is a brilliant, dazzling picture.

"It's beautiful," I say.

"I knew you'd like it," says Molly.

"It's marvellous."

The old lady smiles. "Denzil was very proud of it, it was his favourite picture," she says. "He was a painter too, you know. He was a pupil of Stanhope Forbes, at the Newlyn School."

It suddenly occurs to me: the painting could be Denzil's work. If an unknown artist could paint like this, it would throw everything into confusion. I move closer to examine it, tilting my head back to look through the lower part of my glasses.

"Your brother..." I say. "Your brother didn't paint this?"

"Oh no," says Miss Hooper. "That was painted by Tuke."

I can see the signature, though that does not prove anything. The proof is in the painting itself; everything about it proclaims Henry Scott Tuke.

It is dated 1898. "Has it got a name?" I ask.

"I don't remember a name," she says. "We always called it 'the boys'... But how silly of me! I was forgetting, you really came to see the beach study. Mr Barker, show them the beach study."

Mr Barker struggles in his chair, turning and reaching down to the floor on the far side. He picks up a small picture in a gilt frame and hauls it up, sitting it on his lap so that the light falls on it. It shows a boy, stripped to the waist and wearing a pair of white trousers, sitting on the edge of a rowing boat pulled up on a beach.

"It's lovely," I say, feeling that I am running out of adjectives. I can hardly take my eyes off the large painting on the wall. Two superb Tukes, one large and one small, on the same afternoon; it is too much.

Mr Barker is pushing the beach study forward, resting it on the very edge of his knee. "I'd like you to have it," says Miss Hooper.

I can't believe I have heard her correctly. I look at Mr Barker; his face is impassive, as though he has already been informed of her intentions. I look round at Molly.

"Of course not, Miss Hooper," she says briskly. "It's very kind of you, but you can't go giving your things away, you may need them yet."

"I shan't need this picture, I haven't seen it for years."

"You hold on to it, dear."

"I want to give it to you, you've been very kind to me."

"I can't take it. I'm not allowed to, it's more than my job's worth."

"Then I shall give it to your husband," she says. "It obviously means a lot to him."

Mr Barker lifts the picture and holds it right out. The sunlight shines on the young man's bare skin. It is so much better than the picture in the saleroom. I long to reach out and take it.

"We only wanted to see it," says Molly. "We appreciate seeing your pictures very much. But you must hold on to them."

Slowly, Mr Barker returns the painting to its resting place against his chair. I feel like a child that has been shown a marvellous toy and had it taken away.

"It doesn't mean anything to me," says Miss Hooper.

"Yes it does," says Molly. "You like it because Denzil liked it. You must keep it for his sake."

"I can't keep it for ever."

"You must keep it as long as you can. You mustn't go giving it away. Don't ever show it to anyone who comes knocking at the door asking if you've anything old to sell. Especially if he's called Blake."

I take a last sideways look at the picture on the end wall and at the *Beach Study* that had nearly been mine.

"You couldn't possibly take it," says Molly in the car.

"Oh no," I agree.

"I mean, I was in uniform, it would have been quite wrong. I shouldn't even have taken you there."

"We never knew she would do that."

"She must be more senile than I thought."

"It was astonishing to find the bathing scene."

I can't wait to get to the registers. As soon as we reach home, I look to see what Tuke was painting around the turn of the century. *Sea-Pinks*: Georgy Fouracre stripped among sea pinks and grey stones. His models at the time were mainly Georgy Fouracre and Johnny Jackett: Georgy in a boat sculling, Johnny on the beach in the sun... Lowestoft boats, an Italian barque, Plymouth trawlers... several portraits, a green barque... *The Diver*, begun in April 1898 and resumed summer 1898. I glance on to the content: 'Five boys in foreground; from left 2nd stands back view, as if to dive. 3, 4, 5 in boat with stern sail set. 5th sits in stern, wearing white trousers and hat.'

"Molly," I shout. "Come quickly, I've found it!"

"What is it?" she asks.

"It's *The Diver*, it must be. Five boys, one diving and three in the boat, that's it exactly. But how did Denzil Hooper get hold of it? Why isn't it in a major collection?"

We look back at the register. It was painted on Newporth beach, with Johnny Jackett as the model for two of the figures; the others were Georgy Fouracre, Charlie Mitchell and Bruce Hoskin. It was exhibited at the Royal Academy in 1899, and then shown in Liverpool, Oldham and Pittsburgh. But who does it belong to? 'This picture, according to nephew Geoffrey Sainsbury, 3/7/1963, disappeared in the early nineteen thirties from those for sale by the family.'

I look up the catalogue of the exhibition at the Cooling Galleries, New Bond Street, in 1929, of the pictures remaining in Tuke's possession at the time of his death. The first oil painting listed is *The Diver*, at four hundred guineas. Somehow, Denzil must have acquired it after the sale. I realise that it is the picture the *Cornish Echo* found so reprehensible: 'One cannot help feeling regret that he does not give his attention to a more acceptable subject.'

"My god, Molly," I say. "It's a major picture – and we've rediscovered it."

"Are you doing any work these days?" asks Molly.

"Not very much," I admit.

"Because whenever I come into the study you seem to be drawing up catalogues."

"I've been thinking about those pictures a lot."

"It's no good, it's best to forget them. They aren't yours and they never will be."

"I hardly looked at the other pictures in the room. I wonder what else there is... Do you think she'd like to sell any?"

"No!" exclaims Molly. "I'm not going to make her any offers, is that clear?"

"All right," I say.

I feel I have a certain right to the Tukes. I have discovered them, I have tracked them down, through the

Tuke registers and some local knowledge. But if they were ever auctioned, I'd be in the same position as anyone else.

"What will happen to them?" I ask. "Has she got any relatives?"

"I had a word with her," says Molly, "just to check that she has made all her arrangements. She was very worried about Mr Barker, whose name is Charlie, by the way, and on their own they call each other Charlie and Dorothy. He was just an employee and if she died he would have got nothing. He hasn't any relatives in this country, he's a Canadian though he's lost all contact with his family. So she's left everything to him for the rest of his life and when he dies it goes to various charities."

"Which ones?"

"Half to the church and half to the cats' home."

"Oh no!"

10

THE COLLECTOR
Denzil Hooper's story

Denzil Hooper
Ship at Anchor
Watercolour, 13 x 17 in
Signed

"How's Miss Hooper today?"

"Why do you ask?"

"I'd like to know."   I know I'm interested in what happens to her paintings, but I am concerned about her too. I was moved by the picture of this elderly spinster and her gentleman companion – a Canadian lumberjack! – sitting in darkness amongst her brother's paintings.

"She's not very well, she doesn't seem to be pulling round. She seems to have given up the will to live."

"How's Mr Barker?"

"He plods on. She asked him to show me round the house today."

"Really?"

"I thought that would interest you! We went from room to room, drawing back all the curtains. His sight is failing, it's far worse than I thought. I almost had to guide him."

"What did you see?"

"I don't think I should tell you, it'll disturb you too much."

"What was it?"

"Everything, every room had something interesting in it. There was so much that I can't remember it all."

"Which painters?"

"There were at least two by Stanhope Forbes. One was potato-picking above Mount's Bay –"

"That's a good subject."

"– and the other was a woman at a spinning wheel."

"Nice!"

"There was a Harold Harvey of a woman looking into a mirror... and a man gathering apples in an orchard, with a ladder against a tree... and some bathers by Laura Knight."

"Good heavens!"

"And a Lamorna Birch of a river with a fisherman... and a Charles Simpson of cliffs... and some Procters, Dod and Ernest... and more Tukes."

"It's incredible!"

"There were books everywhere, the books illustrated by the Forbes and catalogues and magazines, all the catalogues of the Royal Academy going back to 1880 and row after row of The Studio. You would have been fascinated."

"When did he die?"

"About twenty years ago. I went back to the sitting room and I said, 'Miss Hooper, where's your brother's paintings? I thought you said he painted, and I haven't seen a single one by him.' And do you know what she said?"

"No."

"'Nurse,' she said, 'he destroyed them all.' He got very depressed about his painting, he thought it was out-of-date. He thought that everybody was very critical of it. One day, it would have been in the early sixties, he lit a bonfire in the garden and threw on to it all his canvases, all his watercolours and sketchbooks, his whole life's work. I asked her if he had kept anything, and she showed me one small watercolour that had survived. It was a ship at anchor, just like a Tuke, the same orange rust stains on the side reflected in the water. Everything else had gone up in flames. 'Didn't you stop him?' I asked. 'No,' she said. 'He always did what he wanted to do, I had no influence over him.' He died a few years later."

"It's a sad story," I say.

Feeling depressed, I walk the dog to the beach. Denzil Hooper had everything to make his life seem enviable. He had enough inherited wealth to indulge his taste for painting and collecting. He could have had a life like Tuke's; even if his talent was smaller, it was probably equal to that of some of the minor painters, Ayerst Ingram or Hereward Tresidder. But he was not only a lesser Tuke, but a later. Tuke and his generation never had any doubts. Stanhope Forbes always knew whether a painting was good or bad. (He praised several of Denzil's, said Dorothy Hooper.) But Denzil was open to other, more modern, influences. His painting was academic, at a time when that had ceased to be a desirable quality. He lost his belief in what he was doing.

The burning of books is terrible enough, but it is difficult to destroy a whole edition; it only needs one copy to escape for a reprint to be possible. But a picture is the whole act of creation, it is the manuscript before it is duplicated or set in print. To destroy it leaves absolutely nothing.

How could he do it? I wonder, as I sit on the rocks at the side of the cove and watch the waves sweeping on to the beach. What was his state of mind as he threw the paintings on the fire, as he watched the flames lick around the canvas, the subjects disappear? What doubt, what despair, what self-hatred, to deny his whole life's work! It was a sort of suicide.

Later, I go with Molly to see the paintings in the rest of the house. It is a remarkable collection, but all I can think about is the man who gathered them together, and destroyed his own work.

"Are you reading anything these days?" asks Molly.

"Nothing much."

"But you usually read when you aren't writing."

"I've rather lost interest in books."

"That's a shame," says Molly briskly, in a voice she keeps for her patients.

"If I were marooned on a desert island, you could forget about the Bible and Shakespeare, all I'd want would be *Artists of the Newlyn School* and *Painting in Newlyn*."

"You ought to get back to writing."

"I'm only interested in catalogues at the moment."

Molly clicks her tongue impatiently.

11

PAINTERS PAINTING

an exhibition catalogue

Why shouldn't a writer write about writing? He is quite free to do so, of course, and often does, but not without being made to feel that he is breaking some sort of code. This view is encouraged by the critics who write dismissively about another book about writing a book – or not writing a book, as the case may be. They imply that it is merely self-indulgent to imagine that anyone else cares about an author's talent, that the use of a quasi-autobiographical narrator leads to self-pity or self-justification. One of the solutions, traditionally, is for the writer to turn himself into a painter, as DH Lawrence did in *Sons and Lovers*. Or if he must write about writing, he is expected to be ironical about himself; a touch of self-mockery will make the self-concern more acceptable.

Painters, on the other hand, have never felt these constraints. They have always seen the self-portrait as a perfectly proper subject, and they have painted themselves and their studios and their friends at work. They have painted about painting without guilt or inhibition.

When I was invited as the first writer to contribute to this occasional series of *The Individual Eye*, I decided to choose those pictures which celebrated this freedom. The second generation of Newlyn School painters delighted in the life of friendship and artistry which they created in Newlyn and Lamorna before and after the first world war, and it is from their work that I have selected this small exhibition of 'painters painting'.   R.T.

1. Samuel John (Lamorna) Birch, RA
(1869-1955)
The Model, Lamorna Cliffs
Oil on canvas, 20 x 24 in
Signed bottom left, SJ *Lamorna Birch*
Provenance: from the artist's studio
MOLLY AND ROGER TREVAIL

  Lamorna Birch and his student are painting at Lamorna Cove in the early nineteen twenties. Birch is painting the young woman artist who is painting a girl sitting on a rock. The student is Midge Bruford (1902-1958), a school friend of his daughter Mornie. The model is Joan Manning-Saunders, who at the age of fifteen was the youngest artist ever to exhibit at the Royal Academy. The summer light and the joyful colour express delight in painting out of doors.

2. Samuel John (Lamorna) Birch, RA
(1869-1955)
Painting in a wood near Lamorna
Oil on academy board, $8^3/_4$ x $13^1/_2$ in
Signed and dated, SJ *Lamorna Birch* 1908
Inscribed, *With love from John*
Exhibited: Painting in Newlyn 1900-1930, Newlyn and
    Plymouth, 1985; Painting in Newlyn 1880-
    1930, Barbican, London, 1985
PRIVATE COLLECTION

  Who is looking at whom is even more complicated in this picture: the painter sitting at his easel on the right is painting the painter standing at her large canvas in the centre of the picture. She is painting a woman and child sitting on a rug beneath a tree on the left. The woman looks at the child, who looks back at the artist in the middle. There is evidence to suggest that the two painters are Laura and Harold Knight, and that the woman is Birch's wife, Mouse, with their daughter, Mornie. Mornie was born in 1904, and the Knights came to Lamorna in 1907. Laura has written that they used to go on picnics together, and it is known that both Laura and Harold painted Mornie when she was four years old.

3. Charles Walter Simpson, RI
(1885-1971)
Mrs Simpson Sketching, Cornwall
Oil on panel, 12 x 16 in
Signed, CW *Simpson*
Provenance: Sotheby's, London, May 1986
PRIVATE COLLECTION

Wearing a beret or tam-o'-shanter, Ruth Simpson (née Alison, 1889-1964), sits on a group of rocks with her back to the artist, facing the sea. She holds a sketching pad in her left hand, resting on her lap. Ruth was a student at the Forbes school of painting when she first met Charles Simpson. "He is awfully clever," she wrote home to her mother, "and has a picture of ducks on the line at the Royal Academy this year. He had another wonderful, huge moorland picture accepted... He is quite young, too – only 28 and is also doing a marvellous 8 foot canvas of life-sized seagulls, blue sea and sunny cliffs." They were married the following year, and this picture was probably painted when they ran the St Ives school of painting. Ruth Simpson specialised in portraiture, and was one of several women artists prominent in the Newlyn school. If the national collections present an image of the artist as male, with only three per cent of the works in public galleries by women artists, then Newlyn helps to redress the balance. Of the twelve painters shown at work in this selection, nine are women and three are men.

4. Charles Walter Simpson, RI
(1885-1971)
Self Portrait
Oil on canvas
Signed
PRIVATE COLLECTION

With soldierly bearing, the artist stares out from the canvas, brushes and palette in his hand, a cigarette between his lips. It was painted in his studio on the harbourside at St Ives, during or just after the first world war. The harbour is in the background, with Smeaton's Pier projecting from the right of the picture. There is something faintly disturbing about this, until you realise that everything seen in the painting is a mirror image.

5. Harold Harvey
(1874-1941)
Laura and Paul Jewill Hill
Oil on canvas, 19 x 17 in
Exhibited: Painting in Newlyn 1900-1930, Newlyn and Plymouth, 1985; Painting in Newlyn 1880-1930, Barbican, London, 1985
PRIVATE COLLECTION

Harvey was a friend of Mr and Mrs Jewill Hill, who commissioned this painting of their two children, Laura and Paul. They are standing at a semi-circular table against a wall; Laura has her weight on one leg and leans with both elbows on the table, her hands around a bowl of goldfish. Paul rests one arm on the table and holds the Italian flag in his hand, celebrating the joining of Italy with the Allies in 1916. Above their heads is a circular mirror in a heavily ornate gilt frame. Seen within it, distorted and in miniature, is the rest of the room, the windows bending with the convexity of the lens. And if you look very closely you can see, just below the centre, the reflection of Harvey himself. He is no larger than the goldfish in the bowl. This ironical self-portrayal is more in the writer's vein than the painter's; if Lamorna Birch is the Lawrence of the artists, then Harold Harvey is the Forster. It is the only self-portrait of him that I know. He more usually painted his artist wife, Gertrude, and her friends.

6. Harold Harvey
(1874-1941)
The Critics
Oil on canvas, 23¼ x 29¾ in
Signed and dated bottom left, Harold Harvey 1922
Provenance: presented to Birmingham City Museum and
                Art Gallery by Sir Barry Jackson, 1922
Exhibited: Royal Academy 1922; Palace of Arts 1938;
                Painting in Newlyn 1900-1930, Newlyn and
                Plymouth, 1985; Painting in Newlyn 1880-
                1930, Barbican, London, 1985
BIRMINGHAM CITY MUSEUM AND ART GALLERY

It is unusual to find a post-war Newlyn picture that tells a story, but here Harvey returns to the Victorian narrative convention and gives it a 1920s setting. Two women are studying the paintings of a third, who sits anxiously awaiting their comments. The woman holding the sketch, which we cannot see, is Gertrude Harvey; she seems to be looking at it rather superciliously, holding it at arm's length in order to evaluate it. Behind her, with one arm on her shoulder and leaning slightly forwards, is Ella Naper (of whom more anon). She looks sympathetically disposed towards the work, whereas Gertrude looks as though she could be waspish, and the apprehension on the unknown artist's face is probably justified. The one example that we can see of her painting seems to be a costume design for a play, or characters in front of a theatre curtain. It contrasts – its position in the composition would seem to make this intentional – with the one picture on the wall, perhaps by Harvey himself, as the viewing is taking place in the Harvey household: Gertrude is very much the hostess in her own home. This picture on the wall is an arid moorland landscape; its tasteful dullness is quite striking, and must be another of Harvey's ironical jokes. The room is middle-class, modern and uncluttered. Apart from the painting in a narrow wooden frame, the walls are bare, distempered rather than papered. There are a lot of verticals, the striped curtains at the window, the panelled door seen almost end-on that opens into the hall, the banisters of the staircase beyond. The circular table is highly polished; on the gleaming surface are a bowl of anemones, bowls of fruit and nuts, a box of cigarettes, coffee cups and empty port glasses. The artist awaits the verdict...

7. Harold Knight, RA
(1874-1961)
In The Studio
Oil on canvas, 24 x 20 in
Signed bottom right, Harold Knight

| Provenance: | Christies 10 December 1926 and 9 March 1984 |
| Exhibited: | Royal Academy 1921, Painting in Newlyn 1900-1930, Newlyn and Plymouth, 1985; Painting in Newlyn 1880-1930, Barbican, London, 1985 |

PRIVATE COLLECTION

A corner of the studio. A shelf with bottles of oil and varnish, above it the lower half of portraits in heavy gilt frames. Some canvases stacked facing the wall. A chair with a heavy coat in check material lying across it, and on top a fur-trimmed hat. A woman sits on a stool, her back three-quarters towards the viewer, and reaches down to hold the heel of her shoe. There is a sense of refinement about the movement, a certain reluctance to proceed. 'I am not used to lowering myself to this sort of thing,' she seems to say, and it gives the picture a faint buzz of eroticism. Is she merely tired after a long sitting and now getting dressed again? Or is she with some hesitation getting undressed for the beginning of a sitting? There is really no ambiguity: she is in the middle of a sitting, holding a pose in which she reaches down to her shoe, as though about to put it on – or take it off.

8. Dame Laura Knight, RA, RWS, RI, RWA, PSWA
(1877-1972)
Reflections
Oil on canvas, 50 x 40 in
Signed bottom right, *Laura Knight*

Exhibited:	Painting in Newlyn 1900-1930, Newlyn and Plymouth 1985; Painting in Newlyn 1880-1930, Barbican, London, 1985
Provenance:	Ex collection of Hon Mrs April Agnes Somerville

JOHN NOOTT FINE PAINTINGS

An unusually self-effacing self-portrait of Laura Knight appears in this painting, in the manner of Harold Harvey's self-portrait in the picture of the Jewill Hill children. This extrovert painter more typically places herself in the foreground of her pictures, as in *Penzance Fair* 1916 or *Self and Nude*. It was painted in 1911 and explores the complex relationship between artist and model. As in the Harvey picture, there are two children, a boy and a girl. The girl sits at the bottom left, looking down into her lap and disappearing off the canvas. Behind her head is the heavy gilt frame of a mirror that fills most of the picture; a boy sits staring into it, profil perdu, watching the painter at work. His full face looks out of the shadows of the glass at the viewer.

Further into the darkness, the light just catches the edge of a canvas and a hand reaching towards it; it catches a scarf at a neck, but no more than a ghostly reflection of the painter in the dark recesses of the mirror.

9. Dame Laura Knight, RA, RWS, RI, RWA, PSWA
(1877-1972)
Self and Nude
Oil on canvas, 60 x 50¹/₄ in
Signed, *Laura Knight*

Exhibited:	*Dame Laura Knight*, Royal Academy 1965; *Dame Laura Knight*, Nottingham Castle 1970; *Artists at Work*, National Portrait Gallery 1981-1982; Painting in Newlyn 1900-1930, Newlyn and Plymouth, 1985; Painting in Newlyn 1880-1930, Barbican, London, 1985
Provenance:	bought via Leger Galleries from Laura Knight's studio sale, Sotheby's November 1970

NATIONAL PORTRAIT GALLERY, LONDON

Painted in 1913, this picture continues Laura Knight's exploration of the relationship between painter and model. She brings herself out of the shadows and places herself firmly in the foreground, filling most of the left-hand side of the canvas to the bottom. The right-hand side to the top is filled by her nude model, who is Ella Naper (1886-1972) again; she poses with her back to the artist, the top half of her body turned slightly towards the centre and her hands clasped behind her head. She stands on a striped mat in front of an orange screen against which her body is sharply outlined. The fold of the screen divides the picture down the middle; the two halves are unified by the repetition of the pose on the canvas in the other half, a painting of a painting, and by Laura Knight's gaze to the right. She too is seen from behind, though her head is turned and seen in profile. Her clothes are as striking as the model's nakedness; she wears a large black hat and a red cardigan (which appears in several of her paintings including *Penzance Fair*. It was bought in a Penzance sale for half a crown, and was also painted by Harold Harvey when his wife Gertrude borrowed it). Laura, who is holding a paintbrush in her hand, is not looking at the model but off-stage. It is difficult to imagine what arrangement of mirrors could have composed this picture: she would seem to have had a mirror behind her which, slightly angled, reflected into another angled mirror to her right. In this case she is painting a reflection of a reflection, which corrects the mirror image: the brush is in her right hand.

10. Charles Naper
(1882-1968)
Ella Playing the Mouth Organ, Dozmary Pool
Oil on canvas, 15^1/$_2$ x 12^1/$_2$ in

Exhibited: Painting in Newlyn 1900-1930, Newlyn and
                 Plymouth, 1985; Painting in Newlyn 1880-
                 1930, Barbican, London, 1985
Provenance: through the artist's family
PRIVATE COLLECTION

Finally, I have chosen this picture because it gives me an opportunity to include the delightful Ella Naper (1886-1972) once more. On the northern edge of Dozmary Pool on Bodmin Moor, Charles and Ella Naper built a wooden hut where, during the summers before the first world war they would spend their holidays, together with the Harveys and the Knights. Laura described them setting off in their Belsize car laden with mattresses, bedding and cooking equipment and with 'Charles Naper in the dickey-seat wrapped round with an old red eiderdown'. The Knights at first camped in a tent until they built their own hut, and the Harveys stayed at a nearby farm. For several weeks they would lead a free existence, painting, swimming, fishing in the pool and cooking their food in the Napers' hut. In this picture, painted in 1912, Ella is seen inside the hut, her hair tied back with a scarf, wearing a loose sweater and long skirt. She is perched on the edge of a table, surrounded by the accoutrements of the simple life, teapot and mugs, jug and bowls, a kettle on a Primus stove, and she is playing a mouth organ that looks like the pipes of Pan. She has a faun-like air; there is something androgynous about her, the skirt could be corduroy trousers.

She also appears in Laura Knight's *Spring* of 1916 which is in the Tate Gallery. There must be a lot of people who remember Ella Naper as an old lady, living in the house at Trewoofe ('Trove') above Lamorna that she and Charles built in 1913 and where they lived for the rest of their lives. But for me, who only know her through the paintings she sat for and through photographs, she is forever youthful, with her slender figure and gamine looks. There is a photograph of a luncheon party in Charles Simpson's studio in St Ives: Simpson stands, a cigarette between his lips, drawing a cork from a bottle, while his dozen guests sit around two tables. Ella sits in a low armchair on the right, leaning slightly forwards, her hands clasped over her knee, her legs crossed, a neat ankle showing above the suspended foot. Amongst all these people, the bearded men and heavily-bosomed women, she looks like a child who for fun has dressed up as an adult. The cloche-like hat obscures her face almost completely, her clothes hang loosely on her slender frame. Her pose suggests eagerness and tension.

She was a jeweller rather than a painter; she made hair combs and slides out of horn, buckles of embossed copper, rings of gold and silver set with stones, enamel earrings and brooches. She taught enamelling to Laura Knight and they made some joint pieces inspired by the Russian

Ballet. She also made some portrait figures of herself and Laura in earthenware with a bright overglaze. Between the wars she ran a pottery, producing teapots, jugs and bowls decorated with bold, colourful flower designs. She made her own clothes. She created a garden.

I adore her. But there is one event in her life that I cannot understand. Her work was widely exhibited; it sold at Liberty's and she had private and public commissions. Charles Naper painted mostly landscapes, spending years making detailed studies of rock formations near Land's End. He exhibited at the Royal Academy between 1910 and 1933, but he sold very little of his work. Ella's jewellery was the main source of their income. One day, when builders were coming to do some repairs to the studio at Trewoofe, he could not bear the thought of anyone seeing his paintings. He took them into the garden and burned them.

How could she have let him do it?

12

MEMORIES OF NEWLYN

an interview

Thomas Cooper Gotch
A Village Carnival
Oil on canvas, 12 x 18 in
Signed, TC Gotch 1884
Exhibited: Memorial Exhibition, Kettering, 1932; West
Cornwall Arts Centre, 1972; Artists of the
Newlyn School 1880-1900, Newlyn, Plymouth
and Bristol, 1979
Provenance: *gift of the artist's daughter*
MRS RENEE NASH

The end of the month is the end of the nurses' year.
Molly has several days leave that she hasn't taken and she
needs to reduce the number of days that she has built up 'in
lieu' of overtime. She takes two weeks' holiday.

"Just because I'm on holiday, that doesn't mean that
you can't work," she says.

"I've nothing to write."

"You've always found something before."

I mow the grass, sow runner beans and lettuce seed.
Molly goes to see some of her patients. "It's a chance to take
my time," she explains. "I'm always rushing in and out. Now I
can sit down and give them my attention."

"I'm getting bored," I say, after a few days' holiday. "I
wish the children would write."

"They're not writers."

"They could drop a line."

"You can't make them."

"What I need is some picture talk, some picture interest." I need something more than my catalogues, and there are no sales, no exhibitions, no galleries worth visiting.

"We could go and see Mrs Nash, if you like."

"Aren't you going anywhere?"

"I was going to see Miss Hooper, but I can always leave it."

Mrs Renee Nash has lived in Newlyn all her life, and has worked for several of the artists in various capacities. For some time we have meant to show her our Fred Evans paintings, to see if she can identify the models. She has said, through a mutual acquaintance, that she would be pleased to help.

She lives in a small terrace house; traffic roars past on the road outside. It seems unlikely that she will hear us knocking on the door. Molly walks in, calling "Hullo, hullo! Is anyone at home?" I follow with the paintings.

A voice replies from a room at the back and we go in; it is stifling hot. "Hullo, dear," says Molly. "Don't get up." Renee has bad legs.

Molly explains who we are. "I've been wanting to meet you for a long time," I say. "I hope it's not inconvenient."

"It's lucky you've caught me. I was about to go down to the Mission –"

"Oh please, don't change your plans for us, we could come another time."

"No, I'd much rather stay and talk, I love a talk."

She talks fluently. It all sounds rather practised, as though she has told her stories many times and they have become polished in the telling. She knows exactly what people want to hear. She is used to being recorded and her voice sounds rather like a tape that has been switched on.

"The BBC wanted to put me on film," she says. "I wasn't very keen at first and they sent two young men to persuade me. Now if there's anything I like more than a handsome young man, 'tis two handsome young men! They did the filming in the gallery. There was a young man with a clapperboard. 'Don't think I don't know what a clapperboard is for, young man,' I said to 'un. 'But I'm not having that thing snapped in front of my nose. There's no need for it!' It took seven of them to do the filming. 'No wonder my television licence costs so much!' I said. I gave five of them their cards, there and then. 'You aren't doing anything,' I said. 'There's no need for you, or you. You can all go.'"

She relishes all the attention she gets, her fame as the last surviving person to have known most of the Newlyn artists. She looked after the Gotches' home for six years while they were away; he was president of the overseas artists' association. His daughter, Phyllis, gave her the picture on the wall above her armchair.

I have already noticed the painting. It shows a procession, with orange Chinese lanterns on a purplish darkness; you can just make out the girls in their white dresses and a carthorse drawing a decorated float.

"Would you like to buy it?" she asks teasingly. "You can have it for a thousand pounds."

"Seven hundred and fifty," I say.

"I wouldn't part with it at any price."

There are other paintings in the room. We turn from the lantern parade to one by John Gutteridge Sykes. "I remember hearing Stanhope Forbes and Gotch talking together," she says, "and one of them said, 'You know, Sykes is a damn good painter!'"

"Did you see much of Stanhope Forbes?"

Her best friend was housekeeper to the Forbeses and she often went with her to Higher Faugan. Stanhope – or

'Stannie' as his second wife called him – used to show her the pictures in his studio. She does an imitation of him, putting on a very upper class accent. "'This is one of my dear, *dear* wife's paintings.' He always referred to his first wife, Elizabeth, as his 'dear, *dear* wife' and to his second wife, Maudie, as his 'dear wife'. He had a very high voice, and one day I met him in the lane where some trees had been cut down and he was very upset. 'Oh the poor trees!' he kept saying in a sing-song voice. 'Oh the poor trees!' Maudie painted too, but she wasn't really very good. If it was good, Stannie had probably had a hand in it somewhere."

"What about Charles Simpson?"

"No one can paint ducks like Charles Simpson," she proclaims, as though giving the generally accepted Newlyn opinion.

"Harold Harvey?"

She chuckles. "We had a nickname for him," she says. "Odd-socks Harvey."

There is a modern painting on one of the walls. When she and her husband were living on a pension of five pounds a week, they used to put two shillings a week into an old tin chocolate-box, to save up for a picture. They saved for seven years and then bought a landscape by John Miller.

I bring my pictures forward. She looks hard at the portrait of an old fisherman. "That's somebody Harvey's dad, that's who that is. I don't know his Christian name, but he lived over on the backside – don't think I'm being vulgar, that's what we call it here in Newlyn."

"What about the other one?" It shows an old fisherman demonstrating a knot to a boy in a purple Norfolk jacket and brown corduroy trousers.

"I don't know the old man," she says. "But the boy could be Ena Williams's father. He was the model for the boy at the end of the table in Stanhope Forbes's *The Health of the*

Bride. He was used a lot as a model. Stanhope told me what he liked about him." She makes a round, smoothing gesture with her hands, the same that Forbes would have made. "It was the roundness of his head that he liked. But he made one mistake in painting that boy, he told me. He hadn't got his arm right, it was too short between the shoulder and the elbow. It was the only fault in the picture. 'An artist can always see his own mistakes,' he said. You have a look the next time you see it."

I tell my own Stanhope Forbes story. Elizabeth, his first wife, had a Canadian accent and pronounced her husband's name with all the emphasis on the first syllable, cutting the second very short. One day a builder called William Hosken came to the house to see about some work that the Forbeses wanted carried out; he used to do odd jobs for them and crate their exhibition canvases. Elizabeth showed him into the sitting room and then went to the door. Mr Hosken had just sat down, when she shouted in a loud voice "Stanhope!" He leaped to his feet. She turned around. "Do sit down, Mr Hosken," she said. He sat down and she turned back to the door. "Stanhope!" she shouted. He stood up again. "No, do sit down... Stanhope!" William Hosken left. "Stan'up, sit down, I've had enough of this," he said. "I'm buggerin' off home."

Stanhope Forbes painted a picture of the builder standing with one foot on the bottom rung of a ladder. 'William Hosken,' it is inscribed, 'with his foot on the ladder of Fame.'

I don't think Renee is listening.

13

CHOCOLATE BOX
a review from the *Cornish Echo*

Samuel John Lamorna Birch RA
There'll always be an England
Oil on canvas, 25 x 30in
Signed and dated 1941
Exhibited: Royal Academy, 1941

*A river winds through an idyllic English landscape. The early morning
mist is lifting from the water, though the sky above is bright. White-
washed cottages cling to the slopes of a hill and the trees are pink with
the buds that are about to burst into leaf.*

Roger Trevail's personal selection of pictures, *Painters
Painting*, on show until the end of the month, is unashamedly
nostalgic. Mr Trevail looks back to a time before and after the
first world war when it seemed reasonable for artists to
portray their own set having lots of fun. There are no hints
here of the war which killed four million young men, no
evidence of the harshness of most people's lives, no
recession nor unemployment, no poverty nor inequality.
Instead we see a lot of favoured people enjoying favoured
lives; they paint each other in sunny glades or sunfilled
coves, they admire each other's work in comfortable middle-
class homes, surrounded with comforting middle-class
objects. They are smug and self-satisfied.

There must be a lot of people who share Mr Trevail's
wish to return to these summery, idyllic days, as evinced by

the rising popularity of Newlyn School paintings and the prices that they now fetch. It is a sad reflection upon our times, that so many people look back to a past that was never really like this, except perhaps for a few.

The Newlyn artists were good craftsmen, that cannot be denied; they knew how to draw and how to handle paint. But the case against them is that their vision was too narrow. They chose to paint only what was pretty, the picturesque fishermen and fisherwomen, the attractive coves and coastline of Cornwall, children and young girls. Their work is very easy on the eye; it makes no demands upon the mind.

Roger Trevail was a great editor, assembling a wealth of talent, old and new, in his magazine *Cornubia*. I have always enjoyed his writing, unsentimental and exact. But I am disappointed to find that what he has assembled in this exhibition shows that beneath the surface lies a very soft centre indeed.   J.B.

"Who the hell is J.B.?" I wonder.

14

DISASTER THREATENS

the breaking up of a collection

Walter Langley
Disaster! Scene in a Cornish Fishing Village
Watercolour with scraping over pencil on Whatman paper,
48 x 30¹/₂ *in*
Signed and dated, WALTER LANGLEY 1889
Exhibited: Royal Institute 1889; Manchester 1889;
Birmingham 1890; Paris 1890; Chicago 1893;
Nottingham 1894; Birmingham 1899;
Whitechapel 1902; Rome 1911; Artists of the
Newlyn School 1880-1900, 1958; Artists of the
Newlyn School 1880-1900, Newlyn, Plymouth
and Bristol, 1979; Walter Langley, Exeter and
Birmingham, 1984; Painting in Newlyn 1880-
1930, Barbican, London, 1985
BIRMINGHAM CITY MUSEUM AND ART GALLERY

*A group of people, mainly women and children, shelter behind a sea wall,
over which the waves are breaking. From the expression on their faces, it
is clear that a boat is wrecked and their loved ones are in danger.*

Molly goes back to work after her holiday. On the first
day she comes home to lunch just after one o'clock; the
coffee is made, bread, cheese and salad are on the table.
"Well," she says importantly, ominously, as soon as
she comes in.

"What is it?"

She sits down at the table. "Dorothy Hooper has gone on."

"She's dead?"

"She died two weeks ago, almost as soon as I came off duty. I'm very annoyed about it."

"Why?" I ask. It was hardly her fault.

"They could have let me know, one of the nurses could have given me a ring from the surgery. They said they didn't want to bother me when I was on holiday. I can't understand how I didn't meet any of them in the street. She's dead and buried, and I didn't know anything about it."

"How's Mr Barker?"

"He's terribly upset. As soon as I could I went to see him. He couldn't understand why I hadn't been before, he'd been expecting me every day for two weeks. He'd had to cope with everything himself, it's been too much for him. When I arrived he broke down and cried like a child."

"What a shame!"

"He said Dorothy was taken ill one night. She was struggling for breath, it sounds like typical heart failure. But he didn't call the doctor until the morning. She was taken to hospital but she died later in the day. Now he blames himself for not calling the doctor straightaway, he thinks if he had she might still be alive. I told him, 'Mr Barker,' I said, 'if her heart was as weak as that she would have died anyway. You've no reason to reproach yourself, you did all you could for her.'"

"What will he do now?"

"It's too early to say, he's still grieving. He misses her terribly, they were very close. He can stay on in the house, but it's far too big for him and he seems more frail than ever without having Dorothy to keep him going. I'm sorry I didn't go and see them when I was on holiday."

"You thought of it."

"I know. I went to see all the others, and at the time I knew I ought to be going to see Dorothy and Charles, I felt I was needed there."

"You'll see him now."

"He's upset about something else, it all came out after a while. Some relatives of Miss Hooper turned up at the funeral, two nieces or second cousins, they called her aunt Dorothy. They had never had anything to do with their aunt when she was alive, they had never been to see her."

"Were they really relatives?"

"Oh yes, he had heard of them. They knew they hadn't been left anything in her will, but could they have some memento of their aunt? He was so distressed by her death and thinking that it was all his fault, he told them to take anything they wanted. She had some very nice jewellery and they took all that, and then they saw the pictures on the walls."

"Oh no!"

"He didn't mind them having the jewellery, he thought it was quite right that they should have all her personal bits and pieces, her 'feminine things', as he called them. But now he's worried that he shouldn't have let them take the paintings."

"Have the paintings gone?" I cry.

"They haven't taken all of them. I couldn't leave him and go round the house to see just what has gone, I've only seen the sitting-room."

"Is the Tuke still there?"

"The boy diving into the water is still on the wall. He said they looked at it and thought it was too big."

"Thank god for that!"

"But all the small ones have gone, all the watercolour portraits and ships."

"No!"

"He regrets it now, he wishes he had been firm and refused them. But he was so upset about Dorothy that he couldn't think of anything else at the time."

"What about the beach study?"

"I don't know, I don't know if it was left in the sitting-room or returned to another part of the house. I didn't see it."

"It doesn't sound as though they know anything about paintings, if they left the large Tuke behind. But what a shame to break up the collection, what a disaster!"

The old man is sitting alone in front of the electric fire, the cat on his lap. The skin of his bald head is covered with dark blotches, it is drawn tight over his long face. His bony hands mechanically smooth the cat. He looks much feebler than before.

"I've brought my husband with me, like you asked," says Molly. "He'll go round and see which pictures are missing."

"Will he remember them?" asks Charlie.

"I'll remember them."

"He'll remember them," repeats Molly. "Roger never forgets a picture once he's seen it."

"I wouldn't remember them," says the old man. "I wouldn't know what was there and what had gone."

The walls around me are strikingly bare, with darker patches on the wallpaper where the Tuke watercolours have hung; they must have faded too, I think. The Diver dominates all the more, the naked boys incongruous in the partially emptied room.

While Molly talks to Mr Barker, I start to inspect the other rooms in the house. I feel apprehensive as I enter the dining-room, expecting to find every picture gone. I am relieved to see at a glance, as I switch on the light before drawing the curtains, that nothing has changed. I take my time and examine each picture: the Stanhope Forbes with its farmworkers, the Charles Simpson of cliffs in evening light, the Harold Harvey of cattle and another of Cornish miners. They do not belong to me: why would I feel robbed if the relatives had taken them?

I draw the curtains again and mount the stairs. Everything is in place, the fairground by Ernest Procter, the bathers by Laura Knight. My hopes rise as I reach the landing; here too there are no empty spaces. Perhaps they took no more than the Tuke watercolours from the sitting room, attracted by the manageable size of the frames.

In what was Denzil's study, there are more gaps. Two of the Elizabeth Forbes have gone. Why should they take two book illustrations and leave a third? There seems to be no sense in it. There are gaps too in the bookshelves; I can't tell what is missing, except that the choice seems random.

Dorothy's bedroom has been stripped bare. My heart sinks as I remember all the small oil paintings by Lamorna Birch that it contained, a study of clouds, a moonlit landscape, a girl standing amongst the flowering gorse. The Laura Knight drawings are also missing from the wall on either side of the bedhead, and a Dod Procter of a girl in a petticoat.

The other rooms are untouched. I remember the beach scene by Tuke and go back to Denzil's room, where I find it propped against the desk. I pick it up and hold it to the light. The young man sits waiting on the side of the boat.

I long to possess it. Two previously unknown relatives have come into the house and helped themselves indiscriminately to whatever they wanted. Why shouldn't I take the Tuke? It was offered to me; it belongs to me far more than the Birches and the Knights belong to the nieces. I found it out with love and knowledge, I have a right to it. If I carried it down to the car, now, the old man would never know, he'd think that it had been taken with all the others...

"Roger!" calls Molly from the stairwell. "What are you doing?"

I join them downstairs. "What an age you've been!" she says.

"I've made a list," I say. "They've taken most of the Tuke watercolours, two Elizabeth Forbes illustrations and some books, and all the Birches, the Laura Knight drawings and a Dod Procter from the front bedroom. That's the lot."

"They knew what they were looking for," says Molly.

"They didn't really. They've left others which are far more valuable."

"I'm not letting them have any more," says Mr Barker.

"What do they intend doing with them?" I ask. They seem to have little idea of value; it would be a shame if they offered them to a dealer like Sexton Blake.

"They said they would keep them."

"Where do they live?" I imagine they are from a nearby town; perhaps I could make them an offer.

"Northampton," says Mr Barker.

If they travelled by train, that would explain why they took none of the larger paintings and not even all of the small ones.

"Now you're not to worry any more," says Molly. "It's over and done with and it's not too bad, you've got plenty left. You'll have to say no in future."

"I sure will," says the old man emphatically.

"Are they really his to give away?" I ask as we drive off in the car. "They aren't left to him in trust?"

"The contents are his, he can do what he likes with them," says Molly. "But the house is his only for the rest of his life."

"What would happen if he went into a home? Would the house stay empty?"

"I expect in that case the trust could sell it, but he would have access only to the interest on the money. He wouldn't be able to touch the capital."

"I see."

"I've arranged some help for him. He'll have a home help twice a week to clean for him and do the shopping, but he wants to do his own cooking. Until two weeks ago he did everything for both of them. Now just looking after himself is too much."

15

DEAR ROGER

a letter of rejection

Henry Scott Tuke, RA
The Message
Oil on canvas, 39$\frac{1}{2}$ x 35$\frac{1}{2}$ *in*
Signed and dated, HS Tuke 1890
Exhibited: Dowdeswell's 1890, *Plymouth* 1891, *Bradford*
         1893, *Nottingham* 1894, *Artists of the Newlyn*
         School 1880-1900, *Newlyn, Plymouth and*
         Bristol 1979, *Falmouth* 1980, *Artists of the*
         Newlyn School 1880-1930, *Barbican, London,*
         1985
FALMOUTH ART GALLERY

A woman sits reading a telegram, watched anxiously by her small son.
The uniformed messenger-boy stands in the doorway. It must be bad
news…

Dear Roger,
        It was good to hear from you after all this time and to
know that you are still writing. I enjoyed reading your
collection of short stories very much indeed. They reminded
me of those long-ago days when we first published you.
        There is no need for me to tell you how times have
changed. As you know, short stories have always been
difficult to market, even more so in the present economic
climate. A volume of stories will sell about one third of the
number of copies that a novel would sell, by the same author.

It is therefore viable to publish only collections by best-selling authors.

Although your Trevail family saga has built up a respectable following over the years, it does not sell in anything like the numbers that would justify publishing a collection of short stories. Furthermore, it would appeal to a different sort of audience; in effect, it would be like publishing the work of an unknown writer. This is quite irrespective of the merits of the stories.

If I might be critical for a moment, I did not find them as satisfying as the ones we first published. Those stories had a freshness about them that was most appealing. I did not find the same quality in these latest stories. It seemed to me almost as though they were parodies. For example, in reading a story like Daddy's Painting I was reminded of Katherine Mansfield, without knowing whether this was deliberate on your part or not. Frankly, I felt that they are not strong enough as parodies, and yet not sufficiently interesting in their own right.

As you know, I have always been a great admirer of your work and so it is with great regret that I feel I have to decline the opportunity of publishing your latest manuscript.

With best wishes for the future,

Yours sincerely,

Felicity

P.S.   Why don't you write a novel?

Why don't I write a novel? Because I don't like novels. All that falling in and out of love, marriage and divorce, sex and violence. All those exaggerated emotions and nervous breakdowns, I couldn't be doing with them. And historical novels are even worse. I'm not really interested in writing about art students in Newlyn before the first world war or foxhunting painters between the wars. My heart sinks at the thought of all those stale conventions: 'Good morning, Mr Forbes', 'Good morning, Mr Bramley.' All those 'he said' and 'she said's. All those *adverbs*.

Dod Proctor said of Harold Harvey that he could only paint what he saw in front of him. I think that is the best sort of painting, the best sort of writing. I can only describe what I see in front of me. For many years, that has been the family growing up.

Well, that's all finished now. They have left home and there is no news from the Himalayas, Australia, New York or wherever. I don't know what they are doing, certainly not enough to write about it. (I sometimes wonder if that is why they have gone so far away.)

But I could still write short stories, I thought. I like the short story, it is a novel stripped of all the padding. It is the moment of insight on its own, without the addition of a lot of autobiography or information. I'd rather keep them separate. With no more autobiography, no more information, I could give my time to what I liked best. And now my stories aren't wanted either.

I put on my cap and coat, for there is a chill wind blowing through the valley from the sea, and carry the manuscript, still in the publisher's wrapping, into the orchard. I gather a cardboard box and newspaper from the garden shed and make a fire. Slowly I feed the short stories into the blaze. The pages are compacted and slow to burn. I stir them with my stick and, as I ease the layers, the flames take hold again, guttering in the wind.

I feel quite remote, as though I am watching someone else destroying part of his life's work. It is not me. Flakes of charred paper whirl into the air amongst the branches of the apple trees.

16

THE ONLY FAIR THING

according to Molly

Frederick James McNamara Evans
Portrait of an Old Man
Watercolour, 8 x 6 in
Signed, FM EVANS
ROGER AND MOLLY TREVAIL

"How's Charlie these days?" I ask.

"His sight's deteriorating rapidly. I persuaded him to go to the doctor and he's made a hospital appointment for him. I've promised to take him, he's become very nervous of himself."

"Why's he losing his sight?"

"He's got cataracts on both eyes."

"Oh no!"

"One has been bad for a long time, now the other is getting worse. But he should be able to see again, it's one of the operations that are really successful."

"But at his age, to have to undergo all that!"

"There are lots of old people who have had cataracts removed. Mrs Trewhella is over ninety, and she's delighted with the result."

"I'm furious with him," says Molly. "I take him to the hospital, I go with him to see the eye specialist – and he refuses to have the operation!"

"I don't blame him."

"He didn't say anything to the specialist and let me make all the arrangements with the medical secretary for him to go on the waiting list and then in the car on the way home he suddenly said, 'I'm not going to have the operation.'"

"I'd do the same."

"Of course you wouldn't! It's a very simple operation, it gives you back your sight. It makes life worth living."

"He has a right to refuse."

"'If you don't co-operate with the doctors,' I said, 'they'll lose interest in you, they'll leave you to get on with it.' 'It doesn't make any difference,' he said. 'The waiting list is so long, I'll be dead before my turn comes up.' 'Mr Barker,' I said. 'There's no need to talk like that!'"

"He says today he wants to go into a home, he can't cope with the house any longer. He can't find his way around, he can't keep it tidy, he can't cook. 'If you have the operation, you'll be able to do all these things, you'll be able to stay here,' I said. 'I'll see if I can get you put on the priority list.' 'No,' he said, 'I want to go into a home.' It's usually just the opposite, they want to stay in their own home as long as they can. But I suppose it was never really his own and now it seems like a burden to him. 'I want you to find me a good place,' he said. 'Well, there aren't many I would recommend,' I said. 'There's only the *Stella Maris* where you wouldn't have to share a room, and they've always got a long waiting list.' 'Get me a place there,' he said. 'Are you sure it's what you want?' 'I want to be away from here,' he said."

"Do you know what he's been and done?" exclaims Molly. "He's supposed to be almost blind, incapable of doing anything much for himself and yet he was able to find a 'houses cleared' advertisement in the local paper and ring them up. I could have wrung his neck! They came out like a shot, of course. They offered him five hundred pounds to clear the house, as though they were doing him a favour. 'We'd take the lot, rubbish and all,' they said. They made out that most of it was worthless, there might be one or two things where they'd see their money back. 'It's daylight robbery,' I said. 'I know its robbery,' he said. 'But what good is it to me? You told me that if I go into *Stella Maris* I have to pay until all my money's gone, and then the social services meet the bill. It doesn't make any difference whether I've got five hundred pounds or five thousand.' 'You don't know that you'll get into *Stella Maris*,' I said. 'You may have to go to a home where you'll only have a room to yourself if you pay for it. You want all the money you can get!' 'Oh,' he said. 'I hadn't thought of that.' 'And anyway,' I said. 'Why give it to the dealers? What have they done for you? Have you signed anything?' 'I told them I had to ask my nurse,' he said. 'They're coming back tomorrow.' So he had a bit of sense, after all."

"I made sure I was there when they arrived. They opened the double gates and drove a van right up to the front door, I'm sure they thought they were going to start loading straight away. They came round to the back and had a bit of a shock when they saw me waiting for them in my uniform. I stepped outside, closing the door behind me as though I didn't want Mr Barker to hear. 'I hope you haven't been put to a lot of trouble,' I said. 'He wants us to clear the house,' said one of the two men. 'We've come to load up.' 'Oh dear,' I said. 'I'm afraid he does this.' 'But he gave us the job.' 'It's all in trust,' I said, waving at the house and stretching the point a bit. 'It's not his to sell, it would have to be agreed with the trustees. You'll have to see his solicitor.' Their faces dropped. 'What about our petrol money?' the other man asked. 'The solicitor deals with all that,' I said. 'If you wait a minute I'll get his name and address.' 'Don't bother, missus,' he said. They went back to their van and revved up and tore around the other half of the drive, sending the gravel flying. They shot out of the gates. I felt quite sorry for them and then I thought no, why should I? What they were doing was quite despicable, trying to rob an old man of his money. They knew the contents were worth thousands, I've nothing but contempt for them."

"He's still determined to go into a home. He's a stubborn old man, when he makes his mind up. And it begins to make more and more sense, he really can't cope in that big house on his own. Even if he had the cataract operation and could see what he was doing, it would still be too much for him. He misses Dorothy, she kept him going. But there's no vacancy at the Stella Maris, the sisters look after them so well that nobody dies off. It's a pity, I could see him fitting in quite happily. There are a lot of men whereas most homes are nearly all women, and they can meet for a chat in the common room or go back to their own room if they want to be quiet. It's more like a club. When you think of some of the other places, three to a room, television blaring all day – he'd hate that! 'You stopped me selling to the house clearers,' he said, 'so tell me how I ought to go about it. I want your advice.' 'You should see Dorothy's solicitor,' I said. 'He knows all about her will, he's the one to advise you.' 'I don't want to see him.' 'Then ask your bank manager, that's what these people are there for.' 'But what would *you* say?' 'Don't have anything to do with dealers,' I said, 'any sort of dealer, antique dealers, house clearers, men who come knocking at the door. The only way to get a fair price is through specialist auctioneers, who'll sell the furniture and the pictures separately.'"

I have to agree. Molly is quite right, it is the only fair thing to do.

17
COMINGS AND GOINGS
another dealer

Stanhope Alexander Forbes RA
By Order of the Court
Oil on canvas
Exhibited: *Royal Academy* 1890
WALKER ART GALLERY, LIVERPOOL

*In a low-ceilinged room, an auctioneer sits on a chair on top of a table, his
gavel raised. His assistant holds up a clock, and a few other small
possessions, jugs and silverware, books, bellows and a coalscuttle are in
front of them. The gathering looks very respectable: a vicar and a smartly
dressed lady, some men in top hats, a woman in a cape who is bidding by
raising her hand. But at the back of the room another woman turns her
face away from the scene, and by her side, almost hidden away, a young
girl weeps.*

A vacancy arises at the Stella Maris. Old Mr Hobbs, in
his ninety-fourth year, passes on quietly in his sleep. "Dear
old Mr Hobbs," says Molly. "I remember his ninetieth
birthday. He was still in his own house then, out on top of a
pair of step-ladders cutting the high hedge next to the road."
Nearly all the other old men and women at the head of the
waiting list have passed on too, and Charlie Barker is offered
a place.
    "He wants to get everything settled straight away,"
says Molly. "He says a sale would take too long."
    "So what will he do?"

"He wants someone who will pay cash. I told him I'd get an auctioneer to come and discuss it with him, but I wasn't going to ring up any dealers for him. 'Then I'll look in the paper and ring up myself,' he said. I don't know why I don't just let him go ahead and do it, it's what he wants and it's really no business of mine. But it makes me mad to think of anyone cheating him out of the money."

"It only pays off the home."

"I know, but I want him to have the full value, even if later he pays it all out. He will have been in control of his own affairs."

"It's what he wants, to sell for cash."

"I just can't stand dealers," says Molly.

"How is it left?"

"I thought he meant it when he said he'd call in another house-clearance firm. So I suggested David Cummings."

"Comings and Goings!"

"The old ladies all like him," says Molly, a shade defensively.

You often see his bright red Talbot Rapier parked in the village. Grey-haired, grey-suited, with a black executive case and a smooth, professional manner, he inspires confidence. He is much in demand when electricity bills arrive or rates are due.

"He's good on furniture," I admit. "And china."

"He gives a fair price, as fair as any."

"But what about the pictures?" I feel the back of my throat go dry when I think of anyone else having the chance to make an offer for them. And almost certainly having it accepted.

"Cummings is going to see him this afternoon."

"Will you be there?" I ask.

"It's nothing to do with me."

The thought of David Cummings, with his sleek grey hair and perpetual sunglasses, buying the Tuke and all the other paintings for a few hundred pounds is more than I can bear. "If he wants ready cash," I said, "why don't you offer him a thousand."

"They're worth more than that."

"Comings and Goings won't offer him more."

"I couldn't do it," says Molly. "I'm sure he would accept, but I wouldn't dream of it. It would be abusing the nurse-patient relationship. It would be most unprofessional."

"But Cummings might be carrying them off, even now!"

"No," says Molly. "I made Mr Barker promise not to commit himself. David Cummings will only give him a quotation."

I breathe a sigh of relief, even though the relief is only temporary.

"Have you seen him?"

"Wait a minute!"

"Has Cummings been yet?"

"I've got other things to do, you know. I've got other patients to attend to, besides Charlie Barker."

"But what did he say?"

Molly sits down and kicks off her shoes. She adds more milk to cool her tea, and takes a drink. I wait impatiently.

"Cummings turned up right on time, at two o'clock," she says. "He thought there were some very nice pieces of furniture and he was very interested in the silver and the china. He stayed there a long time, listing items and making calculations. Mr Barker thought that what he didn't take could be left in the house and sold with it. The carpets and fittings are very worn and not worth anything much –"

"What did he say about the pictures?"

"He looked at them. He said he thought they were very interesting, but he wasn't a picture man. The same with the books, he didn't deal in pictures and books."

"He's not touching them?"

"Wait a minute! He offered, I think, one thousand seven hundred and fifty for the furniture."

"That's not too bad, I suppose."

"I don't think it would make all that much more at an auction... Nine hundred and fifty for the silver."

"I've no idea whether that's good or not."

"And two hundred and fifty for the china, say three thousand altogether. 'What about the paintings?' asked Charlie. 'I don't know,' said Cummings. 'I'd rather not touch them, as I don't know what they are worth.'"

"That was honest."

"He told Charlie that in his own interest he ought to put them into a specialist auction, the same with the books."

I feel a grudging respect; I hadn't expected such integrity. "He's quite right," I admit.

"Wait, I haven't finished yet," says Molly. "Mr Barker said he'd think about it and give him a ring. David Cummings left, and then in the late afternoon he rang back. He'd been thinking about the paintings, he said."

"Ah."

"He wasn't certain about them, he thought the Tuke must be a copy –"

"The man's a fool!"

"– and he would be taking a risk, but if Mr Barker wanted to get rid of everything at once, he'd offer another three thousand for the books and paintings, on top of the three thousand he had already offered."

"He mustn't accept," I cry.

"Cummings must have gone home and thought about

it. He probably looked up a few prices in the catalogues, or had a word with a friend. He realised he couldn't go wrong, he'll make much more on the paintings than on all the rest."

"Has he accepted?"

"He'll phone tomorrow."

"Offer him five thousand."

"You haven't got a thousand, leave alone five. We could only go up to eight hundred and fifty at the last sale, we haven't got any more."

"There must be something."

"What?"

It is true, we have no immediately accessible money beyond about a thousand.

"And anyway," says Molly, "even if we had the money, I wouldn't do it."

18

BETRAYAL

moving pictures

Norman Garstin
Her Signal
Oil *on canvas*, 61½ x 44½ *in*
Exhibited: Royal Academy 1892, Liverpool 1892,
 Nottingham 1894, Whitechapel Art Gallery
 1902, Truro 1978, Artists of the Newlyn
 School 1880-1900, Newlyn Plymouth and
 Bristol 1979, Painting in Newlyn 1880-1930,
 Barbican, London 1985
THE ROYAL INSTITUTION OF CORNWALL

An elderly woman sleeps in her chair, while a younger woman signals
with a lamp at the window...

I stay awake half the night. Molly is breathing deeply
at my side. I know what I want to do and the thought of it
makes sleep impossible. I hear one o'clock strike... two...
three. I fall into a fitful sleep after that and the next thing I
know is that Molly is moving around in a dressing gown.

I am out of bed in a flash and into the bathroom. I get
dressed and join Molly at the kitchen table. She has the local
programme on the radio, very low, and is drinking tea. A
paperback novel is open in front of her. She looks surprised
to see me. "I was going to bring you a cup of tea later," she
says. "You're up early today."

"Yes, I want to get on," I say.

"I never know what time you start, really."

"About half past nine."

"I don't believe it. I bet you get later and later. If I came home at ten I expect I'd still find you drinking tea."

"No," I say vaguely. I get the feeling that I am interrupting an early-morning ritual, with the local voices on the radio and the cups of tea and a book, a time to herself that Molly relishes.

"Well, I must be off," she says, when she comes down dressed.

"Where are you going first?"

"I'll do Mrs Hicks as usual, then on to the Tiddys'."

"How are the geese?"

"They're penned up now, but the yard is still filthy, it's deep in oil sludge. Yesterday there was an enormous sow there, it had got out and Edward was trying to recapture it. It kept skipping out of the way and he was getting madder and madder."

"When are you going to the surgery?"

"I'll have to be there by ten-thirty."

"Will you be home for lunch?"

"No, don't wait for me. I've so much to do today, I'd rather work straight through."

"You'll get an ulcer."

"I'll have plenty of cups of tea." She checks her diary and the contents of her pockets; she pulls on her navy-blue coat and her boots. "Goodbye."

As soon as she has gone, I lock up the house and take the car out of the garage. I feel that I am acting furtively, as though I am being unfaithful. Molly has left for the Hickses' and the Tiddys', in the opposite direction to the village, but as I drive the two miles to the village centre I keep thinking that perhaps she has changed her plans, that she has to collect medicines from the surgery, that I shall meet her white Metro around every bend. I react guiltily when a white car comes towards me, until I see it's a Fiesta. I meet nothing else on the road.

I leave the car behind the bottle bank, in the far corner of the car park, where it is least likely to be noticed; I don't want to park right outside the house. The village street is deserted at this time of the morning; the shops are just opening but there are only one or two customers. A van is delivering bread to the village stores. Beyond the pub and the church, I come to the high stone walls of Miss Hooper's house. I glance up and down the road, and slip through the iron gates.

The gloomy building with its curtained windows lies before me, the dark pine trees rising above it. I walk around the unkempt gravel drive towards the side door, feeling as though I am committing a burglary. My throat is so dry I can scarcely swallow. I make an effort to compose myself.

I open the door and call, "Hullo, it's only me!"

There is no one in the kitchen; it does not seem to be the day for the home help. I go through into the dark hall, wondering what I am doing here. I knock on the sitting-room door, and enter.

Charlie Barker is sitting in the same chair and has the cat on his lap. He looks up, but does not seem surprised that someone has come into the room.

"Hullo Mr Barker," I say loudly, jovially. "How are you?"

"Who is it?" he asks.

"Roger," I say.

"Roger?"

"Roger Trevail. I met you before, I came with my wife."

He still looks bewildered.

"The nurse," I say.

"Nurse," he repeats, and his face lights up as understanding dawns. "You're the nurse's husband."

"That's right," I say. "How are you?"

We talk about his health for a while, which soon leads to plans to sell the contents of the house and go into *Stella Maris*. He repeats the offer that David Cummings has made.

"Have you accepted it yet?" I ask.

"No, I shall ring this morning."

"And will you accept?"

"I won't get a better offer."

"You know how much I like your pictures," I say. "Would you be willing to sell them to me, if I offered more than Cummings?"

He doesn't answer.

"I'll offer you five thousand pounds for the pictures and books."

"Five thousand pounds," he repeats.

"That's two thousand more than Cummings."

"Do you mean it?"

"Yes."

He withdraws his hand from the cat. "It's a deal," he says, and we shake on it.

"I've got to get the money together," I say. "Will you give me the rest of the morning to make the arrangements? I'll come back later to let you know. You won't ring Cummings until I've been back, will you? I'll have the cheque before this afternoon."

"Okay," he says.

We shake hands again.

It was easy, I think, as I let myself out; there was no need to feel anxious. I am jubilant as I walk over the gravel to the gate. The pictures are mine. And the old man is two thousand pounds better off. The only person who could be upset is Cummings; in fact he'll be mad when he realises what he has missed. But he is not a picture man, he was not going to buy them in the first place. He has got the furniture he wanted.

Perhaps, though, he will turn up at the house later on this morning; it would make sense from his point of view not to let the old man think too long about it. He could be on his way now, with his chequebook at the ready in his executive case.

And I have still to get the money together. How do you find five thousand pounds at short notice? I can only think of the bank.

There is a small queue outside the local branch, and I stand and wait for it to open. All my feelings of elation are rapidly fading away; I begin to be anxious again. At ten o'clock a man comes out and bolts back the doors; the queue pushes forward. I ought to have phoned, I decide.

The manager walks through. I grab him. "Have you got a few moments?" I ask.

"Have you made an appointment?" he says.

"No, but it won't take a minute." His first appointee has not arrived; we go into his office.

"I want an overdraft of five thousand pounds," I say.

"An overdraft or a loan?"

"Four thousand pounds would do."

"Is it to buy a car?"

"No," I say. "I have a chance to buy some paintings. They're worth very much more. I could sell one or two and get my money back immediately."

The bank manager looks unhappy. It sounds a very speculative enterprise. I should have said I was buying a car.

"I know about pictures," I add.

He has some papers he is looking at, presumably my

account. We have separate accounts and mine does not move very much, either in or out. We tend to live on Molly's.

"You could have a personal loan of up to three thousand pounds," he says.

"I must have at least four."

"There are limits to what I can do," says the manager. "Now if it were your wife, with her regular income –"

"Couldn't I use the house as surety?"

"You could take out a mortgage on the house, if you want to make any extensions or repairs."

"I want to buy some pictures," I say. "If I make out a cheque for five thousand pounds today, what would you do?"

"I wouldn't be able to honour it at the moment."

"But –" I can only think of a ridiculous turn of phrase. "– I'm a man of substance, I have a house and a collection."

"I can authorise an immediate overdraft of up to three thousand pounds, though if you and your wife care to look through these leaflets and make a joint application –"

"Don't bother," I say.

Back in the car park I remember that Molly will be on her way to the surgery for ten-thirty and it is very nearly that time now. I take a circuitous route back to the house through small lanes. As I approach a crossroads, she shoots past the end. I hold my breath, but she has not seen me. I wait a while, then cross and make for home.

Once inside, I despair. What can I do, if the bank won't honour my cheque? I could go back and ask Mr Barker to accept four thousand, which is a thousand better than Cummings's offer. But somehow I've persuaded myself that five thousand pounds is a fair price – which it isn't really – and my conscience won't let me offer less.

I walk around the house, looking at the pictures. I think of the Tukes, the Forbes, the Harveys belonging to the old man to whom they mean so little. I've got to have them, I can't miss this opportunity. I stop in front of the girls on the beach, the Simpson that Eric has admired. He has said that he would be interested if we ever want to sell it. It would be worth sacrificing to gain the others. Seven and a half thousand, I had suggested. Five, he thought was the sort of figure he could start talking about.

I ring Eric's number. He answers and we talk about this and that, and how there is not much interest on the picture front at the moment. If only he could see Denzil Hooper's collection!

"Eric," I ask. "Are you still interested in the Charles Simpson?"

There is a pause. "Are you selling?"

"I've thought about it."

"Mm... I might be interested."

"You thought it was worth from five to seven and a half."

"Mm."

"I could let you have it for five."

"It's a lot of money to find."

"It's the bottom end of the price range."

"I've got all my capital tied up at the moment. I'd like to have it, but I don't think I could find that sort of money."

"Four thousand then. You know you could make a thousand on it straight away."

"It's not a bad offer."

"It's a very good offer. But I'd have to have the cheque today, I'd bring the picture over this afternoon."

"You couldn't wait until next week?"

"No."

"Why are you in such a hurry? Has something else turned up?"

I have no intention of letting him in on the deal. "No," I say. "I just need the money."

"Four thousand pounds."

"Four thousand."

"All right."

I suddenly feel anxious. "You won't go and sell it for four and a half, will you?" I ask. "I'll buy it back for five in a few months."

"You don't need a fine art dealer," says Eric. "What you need is a bloody pawnbroker."

I have a lot to do. I have to take money out of a building society and put it in the bank. I have to take the girls on the beach to Eric and collect his cheque. But first of all I have to fetch the paintings from Charlie Barker.

I lock up the house and tell the dog to guard. I am driving into the village, thinking how embarrassing it would be if Cummings turns up as I am loading the paintings, when I see a white Metro approaching. It is Molly! The lane is narrow; I slow down and pull in until I am brushing the grass at the side. She will expect me to stop; she will wonder what I am doing, why I am not writing. What am I to tell her? Molly is staring straight ahead at the road and whooshes by without giving me a glance. She has not recognised me!

I open the double gates and park by the front door. I give Charlie Barker his cheque for five thousand pounds. "That's two thousand more than Cummings," I emphasise, as though it makes it all right.

"Are you happy with that?" asks Charlie.

"I'm happy if you are."

"Sure," he says.

There is no sign of Comings and Goings, but I want to load the car as quickly as possible. I open the tailgate and lower the back seat, wondering if the large Tuke will fit inside. I hope I won't have to rush around trying to hire a van before the end of the morning. I stagger out with the Tuke first, hardly able to manage it on my own. I see it in the daylight and for a moment I am so thrilled that I forget all my anxiety and haste; then I worry about damaging it in the car. I try to ease it in; it's a tight fit but it just makes it. I hurry around the house, snatching the pictures from the wall and piling them into the back of the estate, one on top of the other, canvases and frames unprotected. I fill cardboard boxes with books, and place them on the floor and the front seat. It is like a raid, I want it to be over as soon as possible. I might even have left one or two things behind.

The bare walls seem a reproach. I draw the curtains against the light and lock and bolt the front door.

"Goodbye, Mr Barker," I call. As I leave, he is ringing Cummings to accept his offer for the furniture, silver and china. I skid on the gravel of the curved drive. I have to leave the car in the street for a moment while I close the gates. It is laden to the roof; I look to left and right to see who is around. The village is deserted, but I feel eyes peering at me from behind lace-curtained windows. I accelerate away.

"Oh god," I say to myself, as I approach the house. "What will Molly think?"

19

WHAT I THINK OF MY HUSBAND
a personal memoir by
Molly Trevail

I enjoy reading, I read about ten books a week. I read very fast and I read anything, long family chronicles and best-sellers, spy stories and detective stories, historical romances, I get through them very quickly. It always surprises me how little Roger reads. He says I read a lot of rubbish and it's true, a lot of it is rubbish, but every so often I feel I want to read something good and then I'll read the complete works of an author, George Eliot, Virginia Woolf, Katherine Mansfield. I like Thomas Hardy – his books, that is. The man himself seems mean and petty, all that's worst in a man's character. I see it a lot in my work, I see a lot of elderly couples and I'm struck time and time again by the number of sweet-tempered women, real dears they are, who have to put up with mean-spirited, selfish old men. I don't think it's anything to do with the age they were born in, I think it's something that can happen to men as they grow older. If they aren't careful, they grow into themselves and lose all their generosity of spirit.

When I read The Older Hardy[1] I thought yes, this is very recognisable. Old men get like this, mean and fussy and pedantic and self-centred. Those who avoid it are super, nicer than old women. But on the whole old women are nicer than old men, just as women are generally nicer than men. I was interested in Hardy's first wife, Emma Lavinia, and was very struck by the fact that she wrote a piece, a sort of memoir, called What I think of my husband. Thomas Hardy read it after her death and he was so upset by it that he destroyed her

[1] R Gittings The Older Hardy Heinemann 1978   R.T.

manuscript, burning it in a great bonfire of diaries and unpublished work. We shall never know what she said, but can guess that she had no illusions about him and saw him clearly for what he was, a mean-spirited old man. How is it that writers can show so much understanding in their books and so little in real life?

Although I like reading, I don't like writing, it doesn't come naturally to me. I can only do it by pretending I'm not writing, by pretending that I'm talking. So what do I really think of my husband? Roger is no Thomas Hardy, he is no genius, but he had talent and it was the real thing. In his first books, in his short stories, he wrote beautifully, he wrote with such understanding. I thought he was a good man. I loved him for his creativity.

I have none, I know. My only gift is for caring. I can make people comfortable, I can cheer them up if they are lonely or afraid or in pain, I can make them want to keep on living. But I can't create anything, I can't write or paint, it's completely foreign to my nature. I probably over-value those who can.

Roger wrote too much, in all that long family saga. It was spun out in book after book, I got tired of seeing myself. But he had to make a living, it was well done and I admired the way he kept at it. The turning point came, I've always thought, when the magazine closed five years ago. The government was cutting back on the arts, like they've cut back since on the health service – all the best things are cut and the money spent on more and more weapons of destruction – and the subsidy was withdrawn. I suppose they thought *Cornubia* had had a good innings, Roger had edited it for twenty years. It balanced his work as a writer, it got him out of himself and he saw a lot of people. He sees nobody now. The second Mrs Hardy asked her husband if he had spoken to anyone at all during the week. "Yes," said Thomas Hardy, "I spoke to the postman." "And what did you say to him?" "I said, 'Good morning.'" "And what did he say to you?" "He said, 'Good morning, Mr Hardy.'"

It was suddenly like that for Roger, he had nothing else to do but sit at his desk and sink more and more into himself. This wouldn't have mattered much if he'd had a book to work on, but it happened at about the same time that his material was drying up. The children were leaving home, he felt that he was too old for adventures on the boat. He had nothing left to write about. I'm sure that when I'm at work he does nothing but draw up lists or make catalogues of paintings.

The obsession with paintings dates from this time, though he had always been interested. It was something that we could share and I didn't discourage him. It was better, I thought, for him to be chasing after paintings than after women. Roger was always very susceptible to a certain sort of artistic woman, very like his first wife who was a jeweller and who was disastrous for him. He needs someone down-to-earth and practical, but he has a yearning for the creative type, like his passion at the moment for Ella Naper. At least that's harmless!

I was not impressed when I found out that he had burned his short stories. It was just play-acting, self-dramatisation. He knew very well that he still had a first draft in longhand put away in a drawer, plus a top copy of the typescript.

I'm sorry that he no longer wants to write. But what I cannot accept is that as he loses the ability to make art he becomes more and more interested in selling it. He could create and now he seems happy to bargain over the creation of others. It doesn't need any special gifts, only an eye for the main chance and a certain ruthlessness. He's proud that he's outwitted Comings and Goings, he used to be proud of what he produced. He's become a knocker, a dealer, another Sexton Blake. And he used to be the real thing!

But I don't just feel sorry for him. I feel betrayed. I couldn't believe it when I came home from work that day and found the study crammed with the Hooper pictures. And then to find that he had sold the girls on the beach, my favourite picture, without even consulting me even though it was half mine. I never thought Roger could have done anything like that.

For years I have complained about the homes that exploit the elderly, the individuals who cheat the old. Now I have done the same. I should never have introduced my husband to one of my patients and allowed him to profit from it. It's no good saying that the patient is two thousand pounds better off, as Roger keeps repeating, that the pictures would have gone to Cummings for less if he hadn't intervened. That's not the point. I was in a position of trust and that trust has been abused.

My work matters a lot to me. My attitude may be too idealistic for today, when private medicine is encouraged and it seems respectable to make a profit from the sick, but I still think there is something sacred about the relationship between nurse and patient. No one in future can have any confidence in my professionalism. My husband has destroyed it and in doing so has destroyed my feelings for him.

They will never be the same again.

20

THE DENZIL HOOPER COLLECTION

an extract from a sale catalogue

The following lots are from a single collection which was formed between the wars and which has remained intact until the present day. All paintings are oil on canvas unless otherwise stated.

317. CHARLES WALTER SIMPSON (1885-1971)
Evening Light at Carn Barges
Signed, 81 cm x 84 cm

Guide price: 1000 – 1500

318. CHARLES WALTER SIMPSON (1885-1971)
Herring Gulls
Gouache on board, signed, 50 cm x 60 cm

Guide price: 500 – 700

319. CHARLES WALTER SIMPSON (1885-1971)
The Stackyard
Signed, 64 cm x 76 cm

Guide price: 1000 – 1500

320. SAMUEL JOHN LAMORNA BIRCH (1869-1955)
The Stream at Clapper Mill, Lamorna
Watercolour heightened with touches of body colour and scraping out
Signed, 25 cm x 34 cm

Guide price: 1000 – 1200

321. SAMUEL JOHN LAMORNA BIRCH (1869-1955)
April Day at Lamorna
Signed, 54 cm x 61 cm

Guide price: 3000 – 4000

322. HAROLD HARVEY (1874-1941)
The Orchard
Signed and dated 1916, 46 cm x 51 cm

Guide price: 5000 – 10000

323. HAROLD HARVEY (1874-1941)
In the Mirror
Signed and dated 1922, 50 cm x 44 cm

Guide price: 10000 – 15000

324. HAROLD HARVEY (1874-1941
Cornish Miners
Signed and dated 1926, 64 cm x 76cm

Guide price: 10000 – 15000

325. ELIZABETH ADELA FORBES (1859-1912)
An illustration to 'King Arthur's Wood', 1904
Black chalk, watercolour and gouache on paper
Signed, 35 cm x 18 cm

Guide price: 700 – 1000

326. STANHOPE ALEXANDER FORBES (1857-1947)
The Spinning Wheel
Signed and dated 1897, 97 cm x 69 cm

Guide price: 5000 – 7000

327. STANHOPE ALEXANDER FORBES (1857-1947)
The Potato Gatherers
Signed and dated 1921, 63 cm x 76 cm

Guide price: 3000 – 5000

328. ERNEST PROCTER (1886-1935)
La Fête Foraine
Oil on panel, signed, 61 cm x 76 cm
Guide price: 7000 – 10000

329. DOD PROCTER (1892-1972)
The Shy Child
Signed and dated 1930, 76 cm x 54 cm
Guide price: 3000 – 4000

330. DAME LAURA KNIGHT (1877-1972)
Bathers
Black chalk and watercolour heightened with bodycolour
Signed and dated 1917, 56 cm x 76 cm
Guide price: 2000 – 3000

331. DAME LAURA KNIGHT (1877-1972)
The Model, Lamorna
Signed, 51 cm x 61 cm
Exhibited: Royal Academy 1918
Guide price: 5000 – 10000

332. HENRY SCOTT TUKE (1858-1929)
Mending Ropes
Signed and dated 95, 54 cm x 30 cm
Guide price: 800 – 1500

333. HENRY SCOTT TUKE (1858-1929)
Schooners
Watercolour, initialled, 20 cm x 37 cm
Guide price: 300 – 500

334. HENRY SCOTT TUKE (1858-1929)
Beach Study
Signed and dated 1927, 41 cm x 31 cm
Guide price: 1500 – 2000

335. HENRY SCOTT TUKE (1858-1929)
The Diver
Signed and dated 1898, 126 cm x 178 cm
Exhibited: Royal Academy 1899
Guide price: 20000 – 25000

336. DENZIL HOOPER (flourished 1920-1950)
Ship at Anchor
Watercolour, signed, 33 cm x 43 cm
Guide price: 20 – 30

21

AFTER THE SALE

Harold Knight
In the Spring
Oil on canvas, 52½ x 62¼ in
Signed, Harold Knight
LAING ART GALLERY, NEWCASTLE UPON TYNE

In dappled sunlight, a man and woman sit drinking tea at a table beneath apple trees in blossom.

I include them all, in the end. They become an embarrassment in the house and I just want to get rid of them. I would like to keep the *Beach Study*, but decide against it. I want nothing left to remind me of the whole incident.

I tell no one but Eric. "My god, what's this?" he exclaims, when he sees the collection. "The British Rail pension fund?"

"The Roger Trevail pension fund," I mutter.

I would like to send the paintings away from the county, to one of the London auction houses, but I leave most of the arrangements to Eric. I do not go to the sale.

I cannot settle to anything in the study, and writing is out of the question. At twelve o'clock I imagine the auctioneer taking his seat on top of the table, with the window behind him. I haven't been to the viewing, so I don't know where the pictures are hung, but I imagine them in a group on the end wall. Two of them will be on easels at the front, beneath spotlights: *The Diver* certainly, and perhaps one of the

Harveys, the bedroom scene of his wife Gertrude and her reflection in the mirror.

I wander around the house. I can't look at any of the paintings for long, they remind me too much of the others. I go into the garden. It is the height of summer now, the trees are in full leaf and block the view of the valley and hillsides; they encroach upon the house and garden, enclosing it in green. The boughs hang low over the long grass, over the hogweed and foxgloves and swathes of dying bluebells. There is much to do, mowing, cutting back and clearing, but I can only think of the sale. I might just as well have gone as stay at home wondering what is happening. But I wouldn't want to be there when the pictures come up. Eric will mark the catalogue for me and drop it in on his way home.

The auctioneer should reach the Hooper pictures some time between three and four o'clock. I get more and more agitated as the middle of the afternoon draws near. I lock the house and walk the dog to the beach. The car park is full. The café is open and the lifeguards are on duty, their red and yellow flag flying from the mast. The tide is out and groups of people are scattered over the rocks or sitting behind windbreaks on the sand.

"Now!" I think. At this moment the Charles Simpson is being sold. "At one thousand pounds... one thousand one hundred... one thousand two hundred... one thousand three hundred." I hear the rap as the auctioneer brings down his gavel. "Sold for one thousand three hundred pounds."

I walk to the headland, past a family playing cricket, past children digging sandpits and channels, which fill with water from the rock pools. A boy is flying a kite; it rises like a white bird up and up and then swoops low over the beach.

"Six thousand five hundred... seven thousand... seven thousand five hundred." A Harold Harvey sells for seven and a half thousand pounds. It is below the guide price, but there are low reserves on them all. I don't want any to be bought in, to appear again at the next sale. I want them all to go today.

They are bidding on a second Harvey... But perhaps they haven't even started yet, I've no means of knowing. Perhaps it is all over.

Between the red and yellow flags, the bathers leap amongst the waves. Further out the surfers are lying on their boards, waiting for the breakers. The roar of the surf is constant.

"It's the turn of the Stanhope Forbes," I think. It's Laura Knight's bathers, it's Tuke's boys swimming from their boat. "For the last time, at seventeen thousand pounds..."

But as I walk back through the valley, I start at the beginning again and feel once more that they are being sold at that very moment. By the time I reach home I am sure that the sale has finished.

The phone soon rings; it is Eric, from a call-box. He sounds excited. "It's amazing," he keeps saying. "I couldn't wait to tell you. The Tuke made a fantastic price, I'm still trembling. It made over a hundred thousand... Yes, one hundred and five thousand... No, I haven't got to wait, I haven't bought anything. I'll see you shortly."

He's beaming when he arrives. "I told you so, the guide prices were too low," he says. "Every picture has sold, most of them way above the estimates." He holds out the catalogue for me to see the prices that he has written down, but I can't take them in. "Congratulations!" He takes my hand and pumps it up and down.

I can't be looking too pleased.

"You aren't disappointed, are you?" he asks. "They're wonderful prices."

"No, they've done very well."

"And the Tuke, that was the surprise of the day.

Though I don't suppose it should be really, it's the best Newlyn School picture to come on the market for years."

"*How* much did it make?"

"One hundred and five thousand pounds. You should have been there, I've never known such tension in a saleroom as it reached ninety thousand. When it sold everyone broke out clapping. It's broken the hundred thousand barrier, it's a new world record."

"Who bought it?"

"Everything went to London dealers. I've worked it out, when you've paid commission and VAT and insurance, you'll have about a quarter of a million."

"It's a lot." I wish it wasn't quite so much, it's more of a mark-up than the bookseller made when selling to the American.

"The Forbes did well," says Eric. "A little while ago they were saying that Harvey would outstrip him."

"What did the *Beach Study* make?"

"Three thousand. The only pictures that kept within the estimates were the Simpsons."

"Do you still have the girls on the beach?"

"Yes."

"I'd like to buy it back, I'll give you six thousand."

"Five..."

"No, six."

"Well, thanks."

"Molly would like to have it again."

Soon after, Molly comes home from work and joins us for a cup of tea at the table under the trees.

"They've all sold," I say.

"Oh yes."

"Here are the prices," says Eric, pushing forward the catalogue on the table and waiting for the ecstatic response.

Molly glances them through with pursed lips and

then pushes the catalogue away. "It's nothing to do with me," she says.

"Aren't you excited?" asks Eric. "You're very cool, both of you. I'd be leaping around for joy if I'd made a deal like that, I'd be over the moon. Look at you both, I'm more excited than either of you. I don't understand you, you've made a quarter of a million."

"I don't want it."

"I've bought you back the girls," I say.

Molly turns on me. "You haven't any right to it at all."

"What do you expect me to do?"

"You could give it back to Charlie Barker."

"I could give it to Cummings," I say. "He's the only one who's lost."

"It belongs to Charlie."

"He didn't want it."

"It doesn't matter whether he wanted it or not, it's his."

"What good would it do him? It would pay for the home, which the social services pay for anyway. Why give it to the social services? Why give it to the government?"

"It doesn't belong to you."

"It doesn't belong to Charlie, for that matter. The only person the paintings really belonged to was Denzil Hooper and he left them to Dorothy. She wanted everything divided between the church and the cats' home. Perhaps that's what you think I ought to do, give it to the cats' home."

"You shouldn't have got involved."

Eric shifts uneasily in his garden chair. "It's nothing to do with me," he says. "But why didn't you keep the pictures? Then there would have been no problem."

"I needed the money."

"You could have sold just one."

"Roger wanted to play the dealer," says Molly. "He

couldn't wait to sell them, to see how much profit he would make."

"It's legal."

"It's legal, but it's immoral. I expected better of you."

"A quarter of a million," says Eric with a laugh. "If I made that on a deal I wouldn't care too much whether it was moral, or even legal."

Two hundred and fifty thousand pounds. It is more than I could ever hope to make in a lifetime of creativity. I don't suppose I shall write any more. There will be no need to, will there?

The three of us sit, ill at ease, on the garden chairs at the white garden table, in a mixture of sunlight and shadow beneath the swaying branches of the trees; the breeze turns up the undersides of the leaves. Three characters in a leafy garden at the height of summer: if it were not for the sense of strain and tension, it could be a painting by a plein-air artist of the beginning of the century. It could be a Harold Harvey, or a Lamorna Birch, or a Laura Knight.

AN ARTIST ON EVERY CORNER
a bibliography

Biographies

Mrs Lionel Birch:	Stanhope A. Forbes ARA and Elizabeth Forbes, ARWS, 1906
Janet Dunbar:	Laura Knight, 1975
Laura Knight:	Oil Paint and Grease Paint, 1936
Alfred Munnings:	An Artist's Life, 1950
	The Second Burst, 1951
Charles Simpson:	The Fields of Home, 1948
Maria Tuke Sainsbury:	Henry Scott Tuke RA, RWS, A Memoir, 1933
Henry Scott Tuke:	The Diary of Henry Scott Tuke 12 March 1899 – 31 December 1905, edited by B.D. Price, Falmouth: Royal Cornwall Polytechnic Society
CE Vulliamy:	Calico Pie, 1940
Bernard Walke:	Twenty Years at St Hilary, 1935

Catalogues

David Messum: A Breath of Fresh Air, 1974

Michael Canney and Patrick Heron:
  Norman and Alethea Garstin, Two Impressionists – Father and Daughter, 1978

Painting in Cornwall, 1890-1930, The Royal Institution of Cornwall, 1978

Caroline Fox and Francis Greenacre:
  Artists of the Newlyn School 1880-1900, 1979

Andrew Greg:	Charles Napier Hemy RA 1841–1917, 1984
Caroline Fox:	Painting in Newlyn 1900-1930, 1985
Hazel Berriman:	Arts and Crafts in Newlyn 1900-1930, 1986
Caroline Fox:	Samuel John Lamorna Birch RA, Galerie George, 1986
Nicholas Underwood:	Alfred Munnings 1878-1959, Manchester City Art Galleries, York and Bath 1987

Other Literature

Laura Knight:	Magic of a Line, 1965
Mrs Alfred Sidgwick:	None Go By
Charles Simpson:	Animal and Bird Painting, 1939
	El Rodeo, 1925
	Emily Bronte, 1929
	Leicestershire and Its Hunts
	The Harboro' Country
	Trencher and Kennel

The Registers of Henry Scott Tuke (1858-1929)
annotated by BD Price, Falmouth: Royal Cornwall Polytechnic Society, 1983

CE Vulliamy, illustrated by Charles Simpson:
Unknown Cornwall, 1925